The Wild Plants of Cape Clear and adjacent Islands of West Cork

by

John Akeroyd (editor)

Lucy Wright Jennifer Shockley Karen Clarke Nick Rowe
Pat Hatch Mike Robinson Beth Milner

Drawings by Elspeth Beckett

Sherkin Island Marine Station, Sherkin Island, Co. Cork, Ireland

1996

Dedicated to the memory of
Eileen Murphy (1941-1979)
Oleg Vladimirovich Polunin (1914-85)

Published by

Sherkin Island Marine Station,

Sherkin Island, Co. Cork, Ireland

Typeset and Layout by Susan Murphy Wickens
Printed by City Print Ltd., Victoria Cross, Cork, Ireland.

ISBN: 1 870492 86 2

FOREWORD

When my late wife Eileen and myself founded Sherkin Island Marine Station in 1975, we did so because we could not understand why so little interest was shown by the scientific world in the natural history of Sherkin and the other islands in Roaringwater Bay. We were two lay people without any scientific or natural history background and in those early days were in awe of the establishment scientists that came to our Station. Soon we realized that, as in every profession, there are the committed and the egotists; fortunately more of the former came to Sherkin. They gave us the ground rules for what we should be attempting to achieve with our Station. The surveys, many on-going, that we have undertaken over the years include Rocky Shore, Plankton, Sponges, Plants, Birds, Otters, Butterflies and Moths.

Oleg Polunin, the noted British botanist, was only 32 years old when he first came to Sherkin Island in 1947 to record its plant life. History has repeated itself in that this present work on the islands of Roaringwater Bay has been compiled by seven botanists, even younger than Polunin, again from outside Ireland. They are Lucy Wright (UK), Jennifer Shockley (USA), Karen Clarke (USA), Nick Rowe (UK), Mike Robinson (UK), Pat Hatch (UK) and Beth Milner (UK).

Why, one must ask, has there been so little interest in the area from the Irish botanical establishment, with the exception of Miss Maura Scannell, late of the National Botanic Gardens in Dublin? Indeed, when one considers that this Flora is one of only a dozen or so Irish Flora to be published during the last 80 years, one must question how healthy are the data on the Irish flora in general and why have so few Floras been published?

True, modern biology has moved from the field into the laboratory, but young people today see nature conservation as an essential facet of their daily lives. They are interested in, and concerned for, plants and animals as they live in the field. The time has come to go back into the field, like the great Irish naturalists of the 19th Century and the first part of this century, in order to understand fully Ireland's plants and animals, one of our nation's most precious natural resources.

We at Sherkin Island Marine Station offer this Flora of Sherkin, Cape Clear and the adjacent islands in West Cork as our contribution to what we hope is a new beginning in the protection by the Irish people of the wealth of wild plants in their countryside.

Finally, I want to pay special tribute to Dr John Akeroyd, who has, over ten years, made visits to Sherkin to record the flora and to advise our young botanists. He has brought to this project many years of research experience on the European, British and Irish floras and a lifetime's interest in wild plants.

We would like to thank sincerely the following sponsors for the generous support we received for the book:

National Parks & Wildlife Service

Department of the Environment

Schering-Plough (Brinny) Co.

Údarás na Gaeltachta

Matt Murphy

PREFACE

I am very pleased to support this publication about the flora of Roaringwater Bay. It has always been accepted that the conservation of nature must be based on accurate up-to-date information and our knowledge of the flora of this part of West Cork will be greatly enhanced by this publication. It is another in a growing list of excellent publication about different facets of our wildlife by the Sherkin Island Marine Station.

I commend the Editor, John Akeroyd, and his fellow authors, Elspeth Beckett for her drawings and the Murphy family of Sherkin Island for a publication which will, no doubt, help to deepen our knowledge and understanding of plant life in this beautiful part of Cork.

Guím gach rath ar an bhfoilseach áin tábhachtach seo. Tá súil agam go mbeidh an-tóir air, ní amháin ó na scoláirí ach ó go leor leor daoine eile, agus go gcabhróidh sé chun spéis i cúrsaí plandaí a athmhúscailt as an nua sa tír seo.

Michael D Higgins, T.D.
Minister for Arts, Culture
and the Gaeltacht

An **Roinn Ealaíon, Cultúir** 7 **Gaeltachta**
DEPARTMENT of ARTS, CULTURE and the GAELTACHT

TABLE OF CONTENTS

PREFACE

This work represents a remarkable meeting of people and place. During the 1960s Oleg Polunin taught me biology at school. Some 15 years earlier, he had made a detailed study of Sherkin and adjacent islands and he often spoke of West Cork, its fine scenery and rich variety of wild plants and animals. Oleg's love and enthusiasm for field botany in the face of 1960s laboratory science encouraged my resolve to devote my career to the study of the European and Mediterranean floras. In 1979, I took up a fellowship at the School of Botany, Trinity College, Dublin, through the good offices of the Irish Department of Education, and thus grew to know Ireland's flora, vegetation and scenery.

I returned to Britain in 1981, but my work has taken me back to Ireland on many occasions. In 1986 I met Matt Murphy through Carol Hora, a mutual friend of Matt, myself and Oleg Polunin (who had alas died the previous year). It was a moving experience to come to Sherkin and to seek the rare plants that Oleg had recorded as a young botanist over 40 years before. I had never expected to be in a position to continue his studies of the flora of the islands of Roaringwater Bay. Oleg had emphasised to me the richness of the wild flowers in West Cork, but even he would have been astonished at the numbers of both common and rare Irish plants that we have found on Sherkin and the other islands. This volume is a tribute to him and to the other botanists and naturalists who have explored the flora of this unspoilt corner of Ireland.

Numerous people have contributed to the success of this ambitious project to record in detail the Flowering Plants, Conifers and Ferns of Roaringwater Bay. All of the work was carried out at Sherkin Island Marine Station, which financed the whole programme of research for the Flora. Each of the young botanists listed on the title page of this Flora spent some months at the Station contributing to this project, which was set in motion from the Station's foundation in 1975. In 1990 Matt Murphy asked me to co-ordinate and assess the plant records and to help with further recording.

I should especially like to thank my seven fellow authors, listed on the title page in the order of their visits, whose magnificent, hard and dedicated botanical work has made this Flora possible. I also thank Joan Lennon, whose 1979 study of the history of the vegetation has been so useful and so illuminating. Others who have made valuable contributions include Khaled Balabil (1985), Jacinta Crowley (1975), Paul Kay (1992), Charlotte Leeder (1991-2), Pat McCarthy (1975), Penny Pagels (1990), Siobhan Ryan (1990) and Pat Whelan (1975). Some surveyed and mapped the vegetation, others listed species, some collected plants and photographs for the herbarium and others made observations as they travelled about the islands. Several were valued companions in the field or spent time in the library and herbarium helping us with our work. Beth Milner gave me much help in preparing the introductory sections and in editing the final draft of the work. Elspeth Beckett is to be congratulated for her beautiful illustrations.

Tony O'Mahony, joint BSBI recorder with Maura Scannell for Co. Cork, generously allowed us access to unpublished data on the flora of Roaringwater Bay, especially Middle Calf, and provided invaluable data on the botanists working in West Cork during the 19th century. Maura Scannell has long been a source of all sorts of information, and I am grateful to her for a warm welcome and many acts of kindness on my visits over a decade and a half to the National Herbarium at Glasnevin. I should also like to thank An Buanchoiste Téarmaíochta (The Permanent Terminology Committee of the Department of Education) for help with Irish names of plants.

Chris Preston determined pondweeds and tasselweeds, as well as commenting on several other plant groups, and he and Peter Wyse Jackson read critically the manuscript of the Flora. Others who have determined individual specimens are David Allen (specialist group: brambles), Arthur Chater (sedges), Tom Cope (grasses), Jeanette Fryer (cotoneasters), Desmond Meikle (willows) and Tony Primavesi (roses). The wardens of Cape Clear Bird Observatory kindly allowed us access to their card index of plant records. Others whose records we have used are acknowledged in the text.

All the Murphy family have provided wonderful support. Matt Murphy and Susan Murphy Wickens especially have given much time and energy in making my visits to Sherkin so pleasurable and valuable, whilst Michael and Robbie Murphy have speedily, skilfully and cheerfully ferried us all around the islands in the Zodiac 'inflatable'. Susan Murphy Wickens typeset the manuscript with great skill and patience.

Finally, I should like to thank the people of the islands. They have remained friendly, courteous and cheerful while we botanists have crawled over their land, climbed their walls and set their dogs barking. This book is, above all, *their* Flora.

John Akeroyd
Tisbury, Wiltshire, U.K.
January 1996

INTRODUCTION

The wild plants of West Cork have received less study than they deserve. Nevertheless there are many hints in the botanical literature of great richness, notably in the intensive study by Polunin (1949, 1950) of the islands of Roaringwater Bay. Research on plants over the last 15 years by young botanists based at Sherkin Island Marine Station has confirmed this richness. The results of their studies are presented here.

We have found a total of 592 different flowering plants, conifers and ferns (including hybrids and subspecies), which is an astonishing figure for an area of some 10 km^2 in Ireland. Indeed, this would be a high figure for a similar-sized area of Britain, which has a larger flora than Ireland. The flora of Roaringwater Bay is thus of immense importance both nationally and internationally. The area is as rich as anywhere in North-Western Europe.

A Flora (note the capital letter) is an inventory of wild plants, by convention the so-called higher plants - flowering plants, conifers and ferns - of a defined area. This Flora covers a small but unique corner of Ireland. Botanical and vegetation surveys were carried out over several field seasons, the work concentrated on Sherkin but with many visits to other islands. The vegetation (the communities formed by plants) was most intensively studied in 1981-2, the flora (the individual plants) in 1990-95. An account of the islands' plant communities is presented here, together with the floristic inventory. We have also drawn on the records of other botanists who have worked in Roaringwater Bay. Their research is detailed in the next section and indicated in the text. The content of the Flora is backed up by the Sherkin Island Marine Station herbarium, which has representative specimens and slides of many of the species listed. The records are all catalogued in a computer database.

It should be noted that the plants of the islands are but a facet of the natural wealth of species and variation within species, that which scientists refer to as *Biodiversity*, of this part of West Cork. Work at Sherkin Island Marine Station has revealed astonishing numbers of seaweeds and marine animals, from shellfish and worms to dolphins and otters, in Roaringwater Bay and adjacent waters. This great wealth of natural diversity is a precious resource for the people of West Cork and Ireland, one that must be conserved wisely for the use and enjoyment of future generations.

RÉAMHRÁ

Is lú an staidéar a rinneadh ar fhlóra Iarthar Chorcaí ná mar a rinneadh ar go leor áiteanna eile in Éirinn. Is iomaí leid atá i litríocht luibheolaíoch na hÉireann, áfach, faoin mórshaibhreas atá sa cheantar, go háirithe sa staidéar a rinne Oleg Polunin, nach maireann, ar oileáin Loch Trasna sna 1940í déanacha. Tá deimhniú ar an saibhreas sin sa taighde a rinne luibheolaithe óga, atá lonnaithe i Stáisiún Mara Inis Arcáin, le cúig bliana déag anuas agus léirítear torthaí a gcuid staidéir anseo.

Cuimsíonn flóra na n-oileán, ar an iomlán, breis agus 592 de phlandaí bláthacha agus de phlandaí raithní, líon iomlán atá ina ábhar iontais in achar talún nach bhfuil ann ach 10km. Is den ríthábhacht ar fad é flóra Loch Trasna mar sin go náisiúnta agus go hidirnáisiúnta araon, agus é chomh saibhir le háit ar bith in iarthuaisceart na hEorpa.

Is é is Flóra ann ná fardal de na plandaí atá in achar ar leith. De réir nóis, is iad na plandaí "is airde" a bhíonn i gceist - Plandaí Bláthacha, Coiniféir agus Plandaí Raithní. Is é atá le feiceáil anseo ná an Flóra i gcearn bheag d'Éirinn, cearn atá uathúil. Rinneadh suirbhéanna luibheolaíocha agus fásra in imeacht iliomad séasúr allamuigh. Ar Inis Arcáin is mó a rinneadh an obair ach gur tugadh go leor cuairteanna ar oileáin eile. Is i 1981-82 is déine a rinneadh staidéar ar an bhfásra agus i 1990-95 ar an bhflóra. Tá cur síos anseo ar phobail phlandaí na n-oileán mar aon leis an bhfardal bláthúil. Bhaineamar leas freisin as taifid luibheolaithe eile a bhí ag obair ann. Tá luslann Stáisiún Mara Inis Arcáin ina taca i leith ábhar an Fhlóra. Tá samplaí agus sleamhnáin inti de go leor de na speicis atá liostaithe.

Tugtar faoi deara nach bhfuil i bplandaí na n-oileán ach gné de mhaoin nádúrtha na speiceas agus den éagsúlacht laistigh de na speicis, den rud a dtugann na heolaithe bithéagsúlacht air, sa chuid seo d'Iarthar Chorcaí. San obair a rinneadh i Stáisiún Mara Inis Arcáin, nochtadh líon dochreidte feamainní agus ainmhithe mara, idir shliogéisc agus phéisteanna, idir dheilfeanna agus dhobharchúnna i Loch Trasna agus sna huiscí in aice láimhe. Acmhainn an-luachmhar do mhuintir Iarthar Chorcaí agus na hÉireann is ea mórshaibhreas na héagsúlachta nádúrtha sin, agus is rud é nach mór a chaomhnú go stuama do na glúine atá romhainn amach le go mbainfidh siad úsáid agus taitneamh as.

THE ENVIRONMENT AND HISTORY OF
ROARINGWATER BAY

Sherkin Island, Cape Clear and Roaringwater Bay lie immediately west of Baltimore in West Cork. Roaringwater Bay, aptly named for its wild appearance during Atlantic gales, has a ragged coastline dominated by an archipelago of islands, of which Cape Clear and Sherkin are the largest, highest and most populous. Like the other great inlets of West Cork and Kerry, it is to the geographer a *ria* or drowned valley, or rather several valleys, since the islands are arranged in a linear pattern corresponding to eroded ridges of higher ground. Cape Clear is the most southerly point in Ireland, apart from Fastnet rock, 10 km to the south-west.

The book covers all the vegetated islands in Roaringwater Bay. These are Sherkin, Cape Clear, the Carthys, the Calfs, Goat, Long, Castle, Horse, the Skeams, Heir, Spanish, Inishleigh, Mannin and several other smaller islands. We have also included some plant records from the adjacent mainland, especially from Ringarogy (an island linked to the mainland by causeway) and Baltimore, the main port serving the islands and the base for the ferry to Sherkin and Cape Clear. As the plant life of Roaringwater Bay is so rich, the Flora also serves as a useful list for much of West Cork.

Climate

Climatic data are available for Roaringwater Bay, as Sherkin Island Marine Station has maintained meteorological records since July 1972. The area has a mild, moist, Atlantic climate, with strong winds, especially during winter months. There are few frosts, and snow is almost unknown, at least at sea level.

Rainfall is high, fed for much of the year by low pressure weather systems over the Atlantic, and dry spells (at least 15 days with less than 1.0 mm of rain) are infrequent. Absolute drought (at least 15 days with less than 0.2 mm of rain) does occur, but never for more than a month at a time (Palmer 1986). Nevertheless, the wind and relatively high sunshine levels have a drying effect on the landscape and vegetation. During the summer months, rocky ground and south-facing slopes dry out, creating the conditions favoured by plants of more southern affinity.

The rain, as in much of Ireland, is not generally heavy but consists of falls of low intensity over extended periods - the 'soft' weather of country people. Annual rainfall recorded on Sherkin ranges from 910.0 mm (1975) to 1392.4 mm (1982), with an average of 1124.8 mm over the years 1972-84. December is the wettest month, with an average rainfall of 136.8 mm; April, with an average of 45.8 mm, is the driest month (Palmer 1986). During the last decade this pattern of wet and dry months has become more erratic. The high rainfall and frequent mists are favourable to plant growth.

It has been said that the weather in western Ireland consists of gales interspersed with windy periods. The worst winds come during the winter months, but summer gales are frequent and can do considerable damage to plants. The flowers and fruits of plants, especially on exposed coasts, are often brown and withered after a period of salt-laden Atlantic winds.

The Atlantic Ocean, together with warm currents derived from the North Atlantic Drift, has a moderating effect on the temperature of coastal areas such as Roaringwater Bay, creating few extremes of climate in either winter or summer. During the period 1975-84 the average air temperature in January and February, the coldest months, was 6.7°C; the average temperature in August, the warmest month, was 15.5°C (Palmer 1995b). Between 1975 and 1994, rarely did the air temperatures fall to 0°C on more than 10 days a year. The last 10 years have seen far fewer frosts (for example, no air frost at all was recorded in 1989), whereas in 1978 and 1979 there were 22 and 26 days of air frost respectively. During the last 20 years, the temperature rarely fell below -4°C, although -7.7°C was recorded in January 1979. Conversely, the temperature in summer rarely rose above 20°C, although 26.4°C was recorded during the famous hot August of 1976.

Sunshine levels in Roaringwater Bay are high - coastal areas usually receive greater amounts of sunshine than those inland. May is by far the sunniest month, but high levels of daily sunshine may be enjoyed from early April through to the end of August (Palmer 1995a). During the last 10 years at least, May has been a particularly sunny and dry month.

Geology and soils

Solid geology

Rocks are one of the most vivid landscape features that impress the visitor to Roaringwater Bay. The large amount of rocky or broken ground covered with shallow soils accounts in some measure for the richness of the flora. Many plants, especially some of the rarer ones that are so characteristic of the islands, are unable to grow in closed grassland swards, amongst dwarf shrubs like heather or gorse, and on deep or peaty soils.

The rocks that make up most of the islands of Roaringwater Bay are Old Red Sandstones of Devonian age, laid down some 350 million years ago. These rock formations, a major geological feature of South-West and South Central Ireland and underlying much of West Cork, comprise part of the Munster Basin, dated to the Middle and early Upper Devonian period (Clayton *et al.* 1980). Running south-west to north-east, from Fastnet rock to Ross Carbery, they are extensively folded and dip south-east at an angle of 70-80°.

The lowest and thickest series of Devonian rocks is the Sherkin Formation, at least 1050 m thick on the east side of Cape Clear (Graham & Reilly 1972). The formation consists for the most part of beds of fine- to medium-grained, grey and greenish-grey sandstones, often slaty, alternating irregularly with purple or sometimes greenish mudstones. Irregular, white veins of quartz infiltrate these beds. The outcrops that form Cape Clear and the greater part of Sherkin demonstrate the most complete and readily interpreted sections. Greenish-grey sandstone from Cape Clear faces public buildings in Skibbereen. The rocks erode to produce rugged scenery of frequently jagged rock outcrops and cliffs. Several of the rarer plant species such as clovers and other leguminous plants, notably Hairy Bird's-foot Trefoil (*Lotus subbiflorus*), are associated with these rocks.

The Sherkin Formation is overlain by the Castlehaven Formation (750 m thick), dominated by fine-grained, purple mudstones. This outcrops to form most of the islands in the Bay north of Cape Clear and Sherkin. A distinctive stratum is the Kiltorcan Beds of yellowish sandstone that outcrop on Heir and Turk Head. On the mainland the Castlehaven Formation extends from Sheeps Head to Seven Heads, south-west of Kinsale. These rocks erode to produce the softer, more gently rounded landscape that can be seen on the islands to the north of Sherkin and also in Farranacoush townland on the most northerly part of Sherkin. One of the rare plants associated with this formation is Spotted Rock-rose (*Tuberaria guttata*), both on Long and Heir and on the Mizen Head peninsula.

The Carthys and Skeams are composed of Carboniferous Slates laid down over the Upper Devonian rocks. These greyish mudstones and slates extend eastwards from the head of Roaringwater Bay, just to the east of Mannin, and from Skibbereen, with a small outcrop at Toe Head. Carboniferous Limestone, which underlies much of lowland Ireland, occurs inland to the east, but does not outcrop in Roaringwater Bay.

Glacial drift and soils

The whole region was glaciated during the Pleistocene, a period that ended only 10,000 years ago. The ice-sheets which moved down from a northerly direction have left evidence in the form of erratic boulders and rocks bearing *striae* or deep scratches. The soils of the islands have developed for the most part from the extensive brown or grey glacial drift deposits of silt, sand, pebbles and small boulders. On the higher ground, the drift is thin or absent, but in some small valleys and depressions glacial material has created deeper, more fertile soils. A good example is the valley on Sherkin that runs between the Abbey and the west end of Kinish Harbour, where deeper soil and shelter from the wind has allowed elm woodland to develop.

The soils of Sherkin and the other islands fall within four main categories (Conry & Ryan 1962). Most are acid and poor in lime, a feature accentuated by the leaching or washing out of lime and other minerals in the wet climate. The four soil categories are:

Schull Series: developed over variable topography but mostly shallow slopes, often with a patchwork of deeper soils and rock outcrops ('Schull Rocky Phase'). They are *brown earths* derived from shales and sandstones, of good depth and crumb structure and with potential for cultivation. Where the ground is rocky, the land has traditionally been used for rough grazing. This soil type is characteristic of much of the northern part of Cape Clear, the Calfs, Long, Castle, most of Horse and the adjacent mainland to the north.

Rosscarbery Series: developed over gently rolling topography, but often with broken ground and many rock outcrops ('Rosscarbery Rocky Phase'). They are *brown podzols*, derived from shales and sandstones, of good depth and drainage but low mineral content. The land has traditionally been used for grazing and cultivation; locally, as on Sherkin and Heir, lime-rich sea-sand was formerly added as a dressing to enhance mineral levels. This soil type covers Sherkin, the Skeams, Heir, Spanish and the adjacent mainland to the east.

Glan Series: developed over flattish topography. They are water-logged *gley* soils, greyish, brown-mottled and poor in minerals. The land is unsuitable for cultivation and has traditionally been used for rough grazing ('rushy pasture'). Much of the western and central part of Horse is of this type.

'Hill and Mountain Complex A': developed over broken or rolling topography, with generally few rock outcrops. They are *podzols*, badly leached and degraded soils, with areas of peat and thin, peaty soils around rock outcrops. The land has traditionally been used for rough grazing and would support some forestry if it were less exposed. This soil type covers Goat and most of the southern and central part of Cape Clear.

The few lakes on the islands contain deposits of silt and peat. The relatively small beach deposits and areas of wind-blown sand are important habitats for plants and support a rich flora of sand-dune species and lime-loving plants. There are some areas of seashore with muddy or gravelly sand that allow the limited development of saltmarshes, such as in the sheltered inlet of Kinish Harbour on Sherkin.

The generally acid nature of the island soils means that few lime-loving plants occur. Salt-spray has an ameliorating effect on acidity, depositing bases (metal ions) but little calcium or lime. Blown sand, with a high shell and hence lime content, is the only lime-rich habitat. Webb (1949) has listed 30 species that are restricted to lime-rich soils in Ireland. Of these, only Colt's-foot (*Tussilago farfara*), Quaking-grass (*Briza media*), Rustyback Fern (*Asplenium ceterach*), Spindle (*Euonymus europaeus*) and two orchids, Pyramidal Orchid (*Anacamptis pyramidalis*) and Autumn Lady's-tresses (*Spiranthes spiralis*) occur in the islands. Two others, Weld (*Reseda luteola*) and Yellow Oat-grass (*Trisetum flavescens*), have been introduced recently.

All of these plants except Autumn Lady's-tresses have a very limited distribution (see Systematic section). Autumn Lady's-tresses is, however, locally common around rock outcrops, on banks and grassy walls by the sea. Several of the base-demanding plants of coastal grassland, such as Crested Hair-grass (*Koeleria macrantha*), Bird's-foot Trefoil (*Lotus corniculatus*) and Kidney Vetch (*Anthyllis vulneraria*), benefit from the higher levels of lime and other minerals provided by salt spray, seaweed fragments and shell debris.

Conversely, 35 of the 46 plants that Webb (1949) lists as restricted to lime-poor soils in Ireland grow in the islands. This is the typical situation over much of West Cork. The mosaic of habitats and soils in the islands, with gradients of exposure, salinity and soil depth, has nevertheless given rise to a rich tapestry of different plants of varying soil requirements.

Human history and land use

West Cork, like the rest of Ireland, has had a complex history of human settlement and invasion. Roaringwater Bay reveals evidence from all eras of human occupation, from the earliest times to the building or refurbishing of second homes in the 1980s and 1990s. Today only Cape Clear (population 130), Sherkin (90), Long (20) and Heir (10) are inhabited. More recently, two households have been re-established on Horse and there is a holiday cottage on both Sandy and Skeam West.

It is clear from the presence of ancient remains that Sherkin and most of the other islands have been inhabited since at least the Bronze Age, 4000-2500 years ago. A passage grave discovered on Cape Clear in 1984 may date from the Neolithic or New Stone Age (4000-2000 B.C.). Christianity arrived early, perhaps on Cape Clear with St Ciaran as early as the 4th century, and trade with further parts of Europe such as Spain in wine and other goods was established by the medieval period. Where people go, they take plants with them, and their cultivation techniques and patterns of land use have drastic effects on native vegetation.

Plants and people

Medicinal or culinary herbs can persist around centres of human activity for centuries. Castles often have special floras of introduced plants brought in by their owners or garrisons. Several Irish plants can indeed be regarded as being typical of medieval, especially Anglo-Norman, castles (Synnott 1979). The Normans arrived early in Roaringwater Bay: they had occupied Long even before the end of the 12th Century. It was though the O'Driscoll (O hEidersceoil) clan that dominated this part of West Cork for some centuries and their tower-house castles are a feature of the coastal countryside. They built the castles that command the harbours of

Baltimore and Sherkin, and Dun an Oir on the north-western corner of Cape Clear. Heir, today often written Hare, is also known as Inish Ui Drisceoil. The clan held out against the English until 1602.

Baltimore castle was occupied by Spanish soldiers in 1601 during the closing phase of Elizabeth's I's wars with the Irish and no doubt visitors such as these brought plants with them, even accidentally. English settlers came in the early 17th century - only to suffer at the hands of some of the last invaders of the area, Algerian pirates, who sacked Baltimore and carried off many of its inhabitants in 1631. The English introduced many plants all over Ireland, including garden flowers and weeds.

Sherkin Castle, the original construction of which dates from the 15th century, has several plants associated with it. The nearby Abbey (strictly a friary), founded in 1460 by one of the O'Driscolls, has a similar flora, but a poorer one, due to tidying and restoration. The most notable plants associated with the Castle are two members of the carrot family with edible leaves, Alexanders (*Smyrnium olusatrum*) and Parsley (*Petroselinum crispum*). The latter grows abundantly on the walls, where it has been known for a century, and has been found nowhere else in the islands apart from a few plants on Skeam West. It was reported by Polunin (1949) also on the walls of the Abbey: it is gone from there now, but Alexanders persists nearby. Another plant associated with the Castle is Horse-radish (*Armoracia rusticana*), noted by Polunin in 1949 and refound in 1995.

Parsley is associated with castles and other ancient ruins in other parts of Ireland and in Britain: for example, Parsley grows on the Rock of Cashel in Co. Tipperary (*fide* JRA) and on the walls of two castles in Co. Sligo, at one of which it has also been known for a century (Cotton & Cawley 1993). Near to the Castle on Sherkin grows another member of the carrot family, Hemlock (*Conium maculatum*), a poisonous plant found by Synnott (1979) to be associated with 18 out of 20 Norman castles that he examined in East Central Ireland.

Humbler cottages, too, have an interesting exotic flora about them. The islands are an Irish stronghold for Wormwood (*Artemisia absinthium*), now scarce in Ireland. This is associated with buildings and ruins, as is the tall, stately Elecampane (*Inula helenium*), especially on Cape Clear, from where it was first reported by Charles Smith, a Cork physician who visited in 1750 (Day & Copinger 1893). Both plants may have had medicinal use: Elecampane for chest and skin complaints, Wormwood for worming and stomach upsets (and perhaps to flavour poteen). Another plant that is locally abundant on Cape Clear is Marsh Mallow (*Althaea officinalis*), long a remedy for coughs and chest complaints that was no doubt needed by islanders living in damp, draughty cottages. The very poisonous Hemlock, too, grows around settlements in the islands and presumably had medicinal use.

Local people have cultivated many plants in their gardens for ornament, which have escaped and are now part of the local flora. Conspicuous naturalised plants include Easter Lily (*Zantedeschia aethiopica*), Soapwort (*Saponaria officinalis*), Dame's-violet (*Hesperis matronalis*) and Pink-sorrel (*Oxalis articulata*). The use of Fuchsia (*Fuchsia magellanica*) as a hedging plant is very striking. This vigorous shrub grows well in the virtually frost-free environment of the islands.

One of the most significant human influences on the flora and vegetation of the islands has been the construction of walls. These are of stone, sometimes (probably the older walls) with earth. In some places they are completely overgrown with vegetation. The crevices of walls are an important habitat for ferns, especially Hay-scented Buckler-fern (*Dryopteris aemula*) and Lanceolate Spleenwort (*Asplenium obovatum* subsp. *lanceolatum*) in unmortared, and Rusty-back Fern in mortared walls. Walls provide a habitat for plants that occur naturally on cliffs and rock outcrops, such as Wall Pennywort (*Umbilicus rupestris*), and many mosses and lichens. The base of walls provides shelter for larger ferns. Grass-covered walls near the sea have a rich flora that includes several annuals that need an open habitat and a thin soil.

Population changes

Sherkin and the other islands have seen great fluctuations of human population. The islands were depopulated by the authorities in 1610 as nests of piracy, but in 1750 Smith reported 400 families on Cape Clear, and by the early 19th century today's empty lands of the west of Ireland were as densely populated as any region of Europe. By the 1840s both Sherkin and Cape Clear had a population of over 1000, with those of Long and Heir greater than 300. Horse boasted a population of 137 (see below). The Calfs had enough farms to warrant a school, established on Middle Calf in 1835 (Lewis 1837).

Smith had noted potatoes on Cape Clear in 1750 - he even reported the stems being used for thatch. Arriving from the Americas in the early 17th century, the potato provided an easily grown crop that thrived in Ireland's moist Atlantic climate. It supported a huge increase in the human population of Ireland during the 18th century. The Potato Famine changed that forever after 1845, but traces of once extensive potato ridges persist today in the west in pastures and even bogland, tragic reminders of that time.

Potato Blight struck Roaringwater Bay in 1846-47. Relics of former lazy beds can be seen in several places: towards the western end of Long their characteristic ridges extend right down to the rocks and shingly sand of the strand. The population of the Bay was once so dense that even small, windswept islands held human communities. Some of these, like the Calfs, must have been unpleasant places in which to live, notably during the long winters of rain and Atlantic gales. The remains of a small farm on precipitous Goat is almost unbelievable today. Yet several of the settlements on the Calfs and Skeams survived until the 1940s. The effect of the Famine and subsequent emigrations can be measured by the population of Sherkin (O'Reilly 1994). In 1841, before the Famine, Sherkin had 249 inhabited houses. In 1871 this had fallen to 81. Today there are 28, with 40 more occupied in summer.

The Famine does not seem to have been quite so bad in the islands as on the mainland, where Skibbereen especially saw terrible suffering. O' Regan (1994) writes: "My grandfather used to say that there was always fish, seaweed and carrigeen [the seaweed, Irish Moss (*Chondrus crispus*)]". Nevertheless, by 1861 the population of Sherkin had practically halved, while that of Cape Clear had been reduced by nearly a third. Over the next century the population of the islands was in steady decline. By the 1950s most of the smaller islands were uninhabited.

A recent article by O'Regan (1994) gives a vivid picture of life on Skeam West until his family (the last inhabitants) left in 1943. Joseph O'Regan was born on the island in 1921 into one of the two families still living there. The families had been able to buy the island from Samuel Townsend of Whitehall under the provisions of the Land Act of 1870. Joseph studied at the school on Heir, sadly standing empty today - but a notable place to look for ferns! It was a hard life, but they had milk, a few eggs (the children were given one for breakfast only on St Patrick's Day and Easter Sunday!), potatoes and a variety of vegetables. They grew wheat and oats, but had no threshing machine until 1939. The weather was a constant problem: "I think people who visit West Skeam don't realise how high the waves are in a winter storm - big waves right over the rocks, just missing the houses and pouring back down onto the strand, quite a lot of water, not just spray. The problem was getting out or going anywhere in bad weather."

This older way of island life was ending when Oleg Polunin made his first visit in 1947. Tillage was still very much in evidence. Cereals, mostly barley with some wheat, had always been grown as well as potatoes. (O'Regan (1994) mentions "a chap on Horse" who grew barley to make poteen, well out of the way of the exciseman!) Polunin made some interesting notes on tillage agriculture, based on conversation with one of the O'Driscolls on Sherkin (see Appendix 2). He was able to collect several unusual weeds from arable land. Today, these weeds are rare or extinct, although some, like Lesser Snapdragon (*Misopates orontium*), Sharp-leaved Fluellen (*Kickxia elatine*) and several fumitories (*Fumaria*), persist in the islands.

Flax is known to have been grown in West Cork from the mid-18th century. Smith observed in 1750: "But what is most pleasing, the linen manufacture has got some footing in this island, for I have seen tolerable crops of flax. Most of the women spin, and, it is said, they purge and whiten their yarn to a degree of perfection, by means of the soft water of the lake [Lough Errul]". In the 18th and 19th Centuries, when Sherkin had its own boatyard at The Dock, ropes were made from locally grown flax (O'Reilly 1994). Another crop that seems to have been important in the late 18th to early 19th Centuries on poor soils in Ireland was buckwheat, now more characteristic of Poland and Ukraine (and Celtic Brittany). No trace of either of these crops survives in Roaringwater Bay.

Natural products too had their uses in the old rural economy. Turf [peat] is scarce on the islands (O'Regan (1994) notes that it was used instead of coal during the 1926 strike by British miners), but Polunin reported that it was still being cut near Lough Ordree on Sherkin in the late 1940s. Seaweed was collected from the strands in winter and spring for use as fertilizer. Sand too was collected from sandy strands and spread on pasture to increase alkalinity and drainage. Polunin recorded its use in cow sheds from where it was spread on the fields with the dung. Reeds were used for thatching on Cape Clear; gorse was gathered and chopped up for animal feed, and had a variety of other uses (see Lucas 1960). Hay was cut from the native grasslands, but even by the time of Polunin's visits the hay meadows were being sown with new, exotic agricultural plants such as improved Rye-grass (*Lolium perenne*), Italian Rye-grass (*L. multiflorum*) and agricultural variants of Common Vetch (*Vicia sativa*). Our own observations suggest that pasture grasses such as Meadow Foxtail (*Alopecurus pratensis*) and Yellow Oat-grass (*Trisetum flavescens*) may still be arriving in the islands.

Agriculture on Sherkin declined after World War II. At the time of Polunin's first visit in 1947, there were still 50 or so smallholdings (Polunin 1949, see Appendix 1 & 2), with horses, cattle, poultry and plots of cereals and potatoes, but this traditional mixed agriculture seems to have declined over the subsequent five years. Following a 1951 visit, O'Donovan & O'Regan (1952) noted that much of the farmland on Sherkin was no longer tilled. They described how some fields were yellow with Fleabane (*Pulicaria dysenterica*), while others were covered with Field Bindweed (*Convolvulus arvensis*) or mats of Restharrow (*Ononis repens*), today a rare plant on the island.

The islands still support livestock, even the smaller, uninhabited ones. The larger inhabited islands all have herds of cattle which are often allowed to wander freely. They have a considerable effect on the plants by grazing, trampling and producing dung. Cattle are selective feeders and certain plants are always avoided, such as rushes. Overgrazing by cattle actively encourages the development of rushy pastures. Their hooves compress and compact the soil (poaching), causing waterlogging in wetter areas which also creates conditions favourable for rushy pastures. Places enriched with their dung are invaded by plants that thrive under nitrogenous conditions, such as nettles and sorrel (*Rumex acetosa*). Goats are grazed on several of the islands, notably Skeam East and Spanish, and sheep are grazed on Castle, Horse, Skeam West and Mannin. There are still a few horses and donkeys, but not enough to have a significant effect on the vegetation.

Cape Clear has a flourishing population of rabbits. They are absent from Sherkin, however. Local people during the time of Polunin's visits, talked of a poisonous plant that causes them to "sicken and die after two months" (see Appendix 1). This story persists today, but we have been unable to establish the identity of this plant or whether there is another factor involved. Hares are scattered through the islands: for example, we have seen them on all three Calfs.

Grazing is important for maintaining the diversity of some of the grasslands and heathlands. The effects of removing larger grazing animals can be seen on islands such as the Carthys and West Calf. Carthys North Island was grazed by sheep until 1981 (Polunin had reported seeing them there) and is now covered by rank grassland dominated by Creeping Bent (*Agrostis stolonifera*) and Red Fescue (*Festuca rubra*). Animal hoofprints create microhabitats for smaller annual plants, especially those that require a waterlogged soil. Some plants are particularly tolerant of trampling and can be abundant in places such as gaps and gates, where animals gather. Examples include Marsh Cudweed (*Gnaphalium uliginosum*) and Swine-cress (*Coronopus squamatus*). Some of the scarcer plants also grow in this habitat, where trampling is less severe: for example, Water Purslane (*Lythrum portula*), Ivy-leaved Water-crowfoot (*Ranunculus hederaceus*) and Allseed (*Radiola linoides*).

The present population of Sherkin, numbering less than 90, earn their living from small-scale farming (mostly suckler and beef cattle), shellfish fisheries and tourism. There is little tillage, only some Fodder Beet for the cattle and a few patches of potatoes. However, many gardens on Sherkin and other inhabited islands have small vegetable patches with a variety of crops. The island attracts numerous visitors in summer and provides a popular excursion for those on holiday in Baltimore. Scrub and bracken are invading former fields, often recruited from the untended hedges. In time patches of woodland may develop, perhaps with Ash, Elder, even Oak and, locally, English Elm. The few rare oaks give a clue as to what might happen in a century or so. This echoes a trend all over Europe, where woodlands are creeping back on to areas that were previously intensively cultivated. Wind and salt-spray of course slows and limits the process in the islands.

Although farming has dominated island life for so long, fishing was formerly a major industry of Roaringwater Bay and contributed greatly to the wealth of the O'Driscolls (O'Reilly 1994). Pilchards were the main catch during the 16th and 17th Centuries; later hake, herring and mackerel were important. Slate was quarried on Sherkin in the 18th and 19th Centuries. The slate quarries can still be seen on the eastern side of Horseshoe Harbour.

Horse has deposits of the copper ore, malachite. Probably mined in the Bronze Age (see below under Vegetation History), this was the basis of a major industry in the mid-19th Century. Horse today is almost uninhabited. Yet Lewis (1837) wrote: "Here are copper mines which yield very pure ore; they were partially worked by Lord Audley, the proprietor of the island, and by the Irish Mining Company, and have been extensively worked by the West Cork Mining Company, which commenced operations in 1835, and soon discovered a large body of ore close to the eastern point of the island, which is sold at Swansea at a high price. About 100 miners are employed, for whom several houses have been erected." The remains of the settlement, the shafts - which are extremely hazardous - and the heaps of spoil are still there. The mine area has an open vegetation with an interesting flora.

VEGETATION

The vegetation of the coasts and islands of West Cork is varied and much of it is relatively undisturbed. The grasslands, heathlands and rocky ground represent natural and semi-natural plant communities that are rich in species.

The islands clearly form a group, but there is great variation between them in landscape and vegetation. The rock is all hard Old Red Sandstone, its greyish and purplish colours complementing the purple heather and yellow gorse to produce a characteristic, mellow blend of colour. On a sunny day, with the sea a rich azure and Mount Gabriel and the high ground on Cape Clear purplish-blue in the distance, the islands present a wonderful sight. The grasslands too are bright with a myriad of colourful flowers. In late May and June they are dotted with orchids.

Sherkin has the most trees and the best developed scrub. Much of the island is sheltered, both by Cape Clear to the west and by the bulk of Slievemore, the island's mountain. It has the largest flora of all the islands, mainly because it has a wide range of vegetation, including grassland over blown sand, extensive coastal heaths, pastures and rock outcrops, marshes, a deep lake (Lough Ordree) with extensive marginal vegetation, and even a few potato patches. Cape Clear has large areas of heathland over high ground, and still has some haymeadows and remnants of a once rich arable weed flora. All the islands have their own special habitats and even some of the smaller islands have plant communities and species not found elsewhere in Roaringwater Bay.

Vegetation history

Analysis of pollen preserved in post-glacial sediments in Lough Ordree, Sherkin, has yielded much information about the history of the vegetation. A 610 cm core of sediment was collected with an auger from one of the reed-beds in the lough and samples from each level examined for pollen under the microscope (Lennon 1981). These tell a fascinating story.

After the glaciers retreated from West Cork some 10,000 years ago, the landscape was gradually covered by a sparse scrub of Birch (*Betula*), Juniper (*Juniperus*) and willows (*Salix*). Of these, only willows now occur in Roaringwater Bay, many of them probably introduced. Grasses were also present in quantity. This scrub was gradually replaced by a deciduous woodland of Hazel (*Corylus avellana*), a small tree that still occurs sparingly on Sherkin, Horse and Spanish. Woodland of Hazel and Oak, probably Sessile Oak (*Quercus petraea*), then expanded. Pines, presumably Scots Pine (*Pinus sylvestris*), were also present at this time, but it would seem at a lower frequency than Oak. This period of woodland expansion was followed by one of considerable retreat, especially of the pines. Native Pine is thought to have disappeared in Ireland by the early Christian era, although there are reports of occasional trees that might have survived in remote parts of the west. As the tree pollen declines in the sequence, pollen of herbaceous (i.e. non-woody) plants increases proportionately.

The loss of woodland cover in and around Roaringwater Bay may have been due to cumulative leaching of minerals on the acid soils, in conjunction with human clearance of trees. Polunin (unpublished notes) reported the remains of trees in peat near Lough Ordree. About 5000 years ago, all over Ireland, the climate became cooler and wetter. This deterioration, combined with the increased human pressure on woodlands, saw the spread of bogland. Tree stumps and wood are the last relics of the trees that preceded the bogs.

The Bronze Age began in Ireland about 4000 years ago. Evidence from other parts of the country (Mitchell 1986) has revealed the growth of sophisticated agricultural techniques, including the coppicing of woodland for brushwood and branches to feed animals, and the construction of raised lazy beds for crops - needed in the wet climate, with often poor drainage. As forests retreated, plants that survive best in unshaded, open habitats, such as the famous wild flowers of the Burren, would have expanded their range. This would have been true even in far West Cork, although the strong, salt-laden winds of the coast would probably always have kept tree cover to a minimum.

A major factor in woodland clearance around Roaringwater Bay appears to have been the mining (fires were lit to fracture the rock) and smelting of copper. Ancient copper mines on

Mount Gabriel, and probably Horse, date from this period. Indeed, during the period 1700-1500 BC, Mount Gabriel seems to have been a veritable 'Copper Belt', producing bronze axes and other goods (O'Brien 1994). Bronze is a copper-tin alloy; the tin probably came from Cornwall. Wood remains preserved in a flooded mine indicate that oak and hazel were the main woods used, also alder, ash, birch, pine and willow. Tree-ring studies suggest that the inhabitants may have managed this important energy source by coppicing (O'Brien 1994).

Around 700 BC, perhaps a little later, the Iron Age reached Ireland via the Celtic migration. Agricultural technology improved, with stronger iron tools and the development of the ard, a primitive plough. By the end of the 4th Century A.D. and through contact with the Roman and Mediterranean world, more modern ploughs had appeared in Ireland, equipped with a coulter or knife to cut through grass roots. This was the beginning of the age of both monasteries and churches (the church on Skeam West dates from the 9th Century) and of the circular *rath* homestead. Woodland retreated further, but seems to have persisted in Munster, where fine forests of Oak and other trees survived until the early 17th Century - not least the famous Strawberry Tree (*Arbutus unedo*), pockets of which persist on the Iveagh Peninsula.

The Iron Age saw the arrival of many crops, such as rye, oats, peas, beans, cabbage and leeks. Babington's Leek (*Allium ampeloprasum* var. *babingtonii*), found at one site on Sherkin, may have arrived in Ireland as an early leek cultivar. It has persisted as a relic of cultivation in the mild climate of western coasts, notably the Aran Islands and adjacent Connemara.

Fewer crops were introduced during the Early Christian and Medieval periods in Ireland. The monastic 'Golden Age' was, however, a time of increased agricultural expansion and productivity. From the 6th Century, ploughs were being equipped with a mouldboard, to turn the sod over. Woodland decreased and the numbers of weeds, opportunist plants that invade cultivated and disturbed ground, increased. The starch-rich seeds of some of these weeds were used as food, such as those of Fat Hen (*Chenopodium album*) and knotgrasses (*Polygonum*) (Mitchell 1986).

The Elizabethan conquest of Ireland, completed in 1603, marked the beginning of the modern rural economy of Ireland. Munster, devastated by the civil and patriotic wars of the late 16th Century, was ripe for development. It was wild, wooded country, still then a haunt of wolves. We have little documentary evidence of the extent of the Munster oakwoods, but place names provide an interesting clue. In Ireland south of the Shannon, the name Daire or Derry ("oak grove") is concentrated in South Kerry and West Cork (McCracken 1971, map 2, pp. 24-5). The new English rulers and their landlords, firmly in control, cleared the great Munster woods ruthlessly. A century and a half of unsustainable woodland exploitation provided the English economy with raw materials for cooperage (barrels), ship-building and the smelting of copper and iron. The growing population stripped the landscape of wood, except perhaps in the well-guarded demesnes of the wealthy.

There has been little change in pollen frequencies in the Sherkin record over the last six to seven centuries, suggesting similar land use over this period. The most recent part of the Lough Ordree core contained pollen of Ash (*Fraxinus excelsior*) and Elder (*Sambucus nigra*), both of which are present on Sherkin today as hedgerow trees. Pollen grains of Sycamore (*Acer pseudoplatanus*), today a widespread tree in the islands, do not appear in the core - they probably arrived in West Cork from the 17th Century. English Elm (*Ulmus procera*) is probably also a relatively recent arrival.

Sedges and grasses are well-represented throughout the sequence, especially in the upper half of the core. Here they are accompanied by a group of weeds of disturbed and cultivated ground, such as docks (*Rumex*) and Ribwort Plantain (*Plantago lanceolata*). Meadowsweet

(*Filipendula ulmeria*) is also well represented, suggesting similar conditions to today. Several aquatic plants that are present in the islands today occur at variable frequencies right through the fossil sequence: bur-reeds (*Sparganium*), pondweeds (*Potamogeton*), water-milfoils (*Myriophyllum*) and White Water-lily (*Nymphaea alba*). White Water-lily still flourishes in Lough Ordree after 10,000 years! Spores of ferns, notably Bracken (*Pteridium aquilinum*), polypodies (*Polypodium*) and Royal Fern (*Osmunda regalis*), also occur throughout the core.

Outline of plant communities

Our knowledge of the vegetation of the islands of Roaringwater Bay derives largely from the detailed studies of Lucy Wright in 1981-2. Lucy Wright summarised her work in a series of coloured maps, now on display at Sherkin Island Marine Station. Some are reproduced (much reduced) here. At the time the classification scheme of the National Vegetation Survey of Britain had not been published. (No Irish survey has ever been published, although a valuable synopsis of Irish vegetation was presented by White & Doyle, in White 1982).

Oleg Polunin, with help from several students, including Don Boulter and Palmer J. Newbould (who both became professors of botany), had initiated studies on the vegetation in 1948-50. This work was not published, but various manuscripts and rough notes made by Polunin and others are available in the Library of the Marine Station. These notes are of great interest, giving a picture of what the vegetation was like nearly 50 years ago (much of it not that different!), and have also yielded some records for the Systematic List (see below).

Lucy Wright's maps are based on the 6" maps of the Ordnance Survey. They show general habitat types, subdivided into vegetation units by species composition. The units were assessed on the basis of major structural features such as dominant plants, life form (annual, herbaceous perennial, shrub) and indicator species. The maps were produced by relatively rapid survey, both to cover the large amount of ground and to provide readily available data for surveys of animals such as insects. Lucy Wright's lists of plants from individual localities in different habitats are kept at Sherkin Island Marine Station.

Below we summarise the main vegetation types of the islands.

I. Woodland

"There are no woodlands of any kind on the islands" observed Polunin in 1950 (Polunin unpublished notes). There are probably many more trees now than there were then, due to natural regrowth and deliberate planting, but the islands remain largely treeless and young trees are prevented from establishing by the strong, salt-laden winds on these exposed coasts. The decline of tillage in the islands and fewer grazing animals over the last 40 years has enabled trees to regenerate and spread on a small scale. However, the only true woodland in the islands is the belt of English Elm on the southern side of Kinish Harbour on Sherkin. Areas of scrub on Spanish are beginning, too, to revert to woodland.

Much of the hilly and mountainous country of Western Ireland was probably once covered with woodland of Sessile Oak, a tree that favours wetter, more acid soils. Before its final clearance in the Iron Age, Scots Pine would also have been locally dominant. Other trees, notably Ash, survive in hedgerows. The pollen sequence that Joan Lennon found in sediments from Lake Ordree (see above) suggests that woodland cover in Roaringwater Bay had largely disappeared many centuries ago, at least in the islands. Polunin (unpublished notes) recorded "numerous examples of buried tree trunks and roots (maximum over 1 ft in diameter)" in peat near Lough Ordree. He suggested that they might be pine or birch.

The high humidity of the Irish climate, particularly in the west, allows the typical plants of the woodland floor to flourish in a wider range of habitats than elsewhere in Europe. For example, in the islands of Roaringwater Bay, Common Dog-violet (*Viola riviniana*), Lesser Celandine (*Ranunculus ficaria*), Earth-nut (*Conopodium majus*) and Primrose (*Primula vulgaris*), all woodland plants, occur in large numbers in grassland and heathland. Other woodland plants such as Bluebell (*Hyacinthoides non-scriptus*) and Wood -sorrel (*Oxalis acetosella*), are found in the open, but mostly under bracken, the fronds of which grow at the time that leaves would be present on deciduous trees.

Although most native Scots Pine is thought to have disappeared from Ireland nearly 2000 years ago, plantations of this and other conifers were established from the 17th century onwards. Today they are the basis of commercial forestry. Sherkin, Cape Clear and Heir have some small plantations and shelter-belts of conifers, mostly the wind- and spray-resistant Monterey Pine (*Pinus radiata*) from the coast of California. Sitka Spruce (*Picea sitchensis*), very tolerant of wet and waterlogged soils, is also widely planted in shelter belts.

II. Scrub

Scrub is especially characteristic of abandoned grazing land. It also develops in shelter along walls and lanes, often with Bramble thickets as a first stage. Hedges provide a supply of fruits for the recruitment of Blackthorn, Elder, Gorse and Hawthorn. Gorse and Blackthorn frequently form thickets. In wetter places, as on parts of Horse, the scrub is dominated by various willows, especially Eared Willow. Few of these scrub communities can be said to represent native vegetation.

More truly native plant communities may survive on cliffs. Here and there on broken, rocky ground on Cape Clear and at Foardree, Sherkin, are pockets of Broom. Blackthorn scrub on cliffs may also be a native community. At the eastern end of Horse is a deep, sheltered gully in a low sea-cliff fringed with a tall scrub of Hazel and Spindle. This may well be a fragment of native vegetation, even if dwarfed Apple trees in a similar seaside gully on Skeam East are a relic of a long-forgotten picnic or a former garden.

On Spanish, where scrub has developed since the abandonment of agriculture, woodland plants persist and flourish in its shade. These include Barren Strawberry (*Potentilla sterilis*), Enchanter's-nightshade (*Circaea lutetiana*), Wood Avens (*Geum urbanum*), Wood Dock (*Rumex sanguineus*) and Wood Sorrel (*Oxalis acetosella*). In fact, Enchanter's-nightshade and Wood Avens have their only stations in the islands here. Other woodland plants, such as Wood Anemone (*Anemone nemorosa*), that Polunin (unpublished notes) recorded in woods at Lough Hyne on the mainland, have not been found.

III. Grassland

Grassland is a most characteristic Irish habitat, promoted by plentiful rain and a long growing season. Grazing prevents the encroachment of scrub or woodland. Much of the grassland on the surviving smallholdings and farms of the islands is improved, in other words it has been resown and had fertilizers added. This encourages the growth of a few species such as Rye-grass (*Lolium perenne*) at the expense of a former diverse flora of grasses and other herbaceous plants. Unimproved, semi-natural grassland survives, however, in the islands of Roaringwater Bay to a considerable extent, mostly grading into heathland near the sea.

The coastal grasslands in the islands are species-rich, colourful and attractive. The sward is dominated by Red Fescue (*Festuca rubra*), with Creeping Bent (*Agrostis stolonifera*), Crested Dog's-tail (*Cynosurus cristatus*) and Sweet Vernal-grass (*Anthoxanthum odoratum*). Non-grasses include Bird's-foot Trefoil (*Lotus corniculatus*), Centaury (*Centaurium erythraea*), Daisy (*Bellis perennis*), Eyebright (*Euphrasia tetraquetra*), Lady's Bedstraw (*Galium verum*), Ox-eye Daisy (*Leucanthemum vulgare*), Sorrel (*Rumex acetosa*), Wild

Carrot (*Daucus carota*) and Yarrow (*Achillea millefolium*). Bulbous Buttercup (*Ranunculus bulbosus*) is prominent earlier in the year.

In grassland over coastal rocks, other plants are Crested Hair-grass (*Koeleria macrantha*), Kidney Vetch (*Anthyllis vulneraria*) and the delicate orchid, Autumn Lady's-tresses (*Spiranthes spiralis*). A similar grassland occurs on earth-covered walls near the sea. These have a number of annual and short-lived perennial plants as well, such as clovers, Field Madder (*Sherardia arvensis*) and Wall Speedwell (*Veronica arvensis*). In spring, these walls and other grassy seaside banks are covered with Primroses (*Primula vulgaris*).

Coastal rocks and cliffs have an open vegetation, basically grassland. The vegetation is dominated by salt-tolerant plants, often with fleshy leaves. The most important of these plants are Thrift (*Armeria maritima*), often growing in large, spongy hummocks, Sea Plantain (*Plantago maritima*), Buckshorn Plantain (*P. coronopus*) and Rock Spurrey (*Spergularia rupicola*). Often, however, the vegetation on cliffs is a more closed turf dominated by a shaggy growth of Red Fescue (*Festuca rubra*). Where there are seabird colonies, a scruffy plant community is dominated by Scurvygrass (*Cochlearia officinalis*), which flowers in early spring, and oraches, nitrogen-demanding annuals which grow up during the summer. A lush variant of Sorrel (*Rumex acetosa*), described by some botanists as a distinct subspecies, is also typical of these cliff swards. The fern Sea Spleenwort (*Asplenium marinum*) is widespread in crevices of rocks near the sea.

The most exposed sites develop a dwarf 'Plantago sward', a carpet-like community originally described by Robert Lloyd Praeger, dominated by the two coastal plantains. Open, gravelly ground at the top of cliffs has Sea Pearlwort (*Sagina maritima*) and other dwarfed annuals. The community grades into a short coastal grassland sward. This is not as extreme on Sherkin as elsewhere in Western Ireland: Praeger described Plantago swards that formed "a shining green carpet ... as smooth to the hand as a newly-ironed table-cloth" (see White & Doyle in White 1982, pp. 105-110). On the steepest cliffs an open vegetation develops with tussocks of grassland species, Sea Campion (*Silene uniflora*), Rock Samphire (*Crithmum maritimum*), Scurvygrass (*Cochlearia officinalis*) and Sea Beet (*Beta vulgaris* subsp. *maritima*).

Grassland over blown sand, for example at Cow and Silver Strands, Sherkin, has Sand Sedge and the orchids Western Marsh-orchid (*Dactylorrhiza majalis* subsp. *occidentalis*) and Pyramidal Orchid (*Anacamptis pyramidalis*). Dune Pansy (*Viola tricolor* subsp. *curtisii*), one of the rarest plants in Roaringwater Bay, survives in sandy grassland on East Calf, and more locally on Horse. Despite repeated searches on Sherkin, it has not been seen there since Polunin's visits. Open ground in sandy coastal grassland is the main habitat for winter annuals such as Wall Speedwell (*Veronica arvensis*) and Sea Mouse-ear Chickweed (*Cerastium diffusum*). These flower in spring and die down when this habitat becomes hot and dry in the summer. Sandy grassland is always a worthwhile place to search for rare or under-recorded plants.

Horse has some of the most interesting grasslands. Much of the central and western part of the island has wet, rushy pastures and dense willow-scrub, but the eastern end and parts of the western (where there is much blown sand) have species-rich grassland. Here occur small populations of Deptford Pink (*Dianthus armeria*), Hop Trefoil (*Trifolium campestre*) and Slender Centaury (*Centaurium pulchellum*). Although the island is no longer farmed, hay is still cut from the grasslands to the south of the main settlement at the eastern end of Horse. Sheep graze the western end.

IV. Heath

Heathlands are an extensive, conspicuous and floristically rich element in the vegetation of the islands. Overall they represent the most important semi-natural vegetation type. On exposed coasts over shallow soils they are the natural vegetation that replaces woodland. Rocky areas within heathland support the most species-rich communities, in which may be found several of the rarest plants of the islands.

The typical coastal heaths of Roaringwater Bay are covered by a low, dense growth of Dwarf Gorse (*Ulex gallii*), Ling (*Calluna vulgaris*) and Bell Heather (*Erica cinerea*), together with the grasses Common Bent (*Agrostis capillaris*), Creeping Bent (*A. stolonifera*) and Sheep's Fescue (*Festuca ovina*), and a few other plants such as Tormentil (*Potentilla erecta*). Some sedges, such as Carnation Sedge (*Carex panicea*) and Green-ribbed Sedge (*C. binervis*) are prominent in this community, as are extensive patches of Creeping Willow (*Salix repens*). This plant community looks its best in late summer when the main species are in flower. On a sunny day, set against an azure sea and the distant dark blue of Mount Gabriel, the coastal heaths are a beautiful sight.

This characteristic plant community is interspersed with grassy areas and rock outcrops. Typical plants of the rock outcrops, which are exposed and dry, with a thin, stony soil, are Cat's-ear (*Hypochoeris radicata*), Sheep's-bit (*Jasione montana*), Sheep's Sorrel (*Rumex acetosella*) and White Stonecrop (*Sedum anglicum*). Other plants of shallow soils on or around rock outcrops include a group of rare clovers and related plants, including Bird's-foot (*Ornithopus perpusillus*) on parts of Sherkin, Long and elsewhere, and Bird's-foot Clover (*T. ornithopodioides*) and Soft Clover (*Trifolium striatum*) at the western end of Sherkin. At South Harbour on Cape Clear and at Foardree and Horseshoe Harbour on Sherkin, the rocky heathland supports a group of rare plants, notably the special rarity, Hairy Bird's-foot Trefoil (*Lotus subbiflorus*).

The heathy grasslands are also rich in plants and can be very colourful in summer. Grasses include Sweet Vernal-grass (*Anthoxanthum odoratum*) and Heath-grass (*Danthonia decumbens*), sometimes with Purple Moor-grass (*Molinia caerulea*). The sward is bright with Cat's-ear, Tormentil, Common Dog-violet (*Viola riviniana*), Heath Milkwort (*Polygala serpyllifolia*), Devil's-bit Scabious (*Succisa pratensis*) and Sorrel (*Rumex acetosa*). These grasslands grade into the more mineral-rich coastal grasslands of seaside rock outcrops, blown sand and wall-tops.

Deeper, more peaty, soils in damp hollows support a plant community dominated by Purple Moor-grass and Cross-leaved heath (*Erica tetralix*). Where the soil is deeper but less damp, Bracken (*Pteridium aquilinum*) invades the heathland. This is especially true of abandoned pasture. When this occurs soil fertility may increase, which can make re-establishment of the original habitat difficult in the long term. Heathlands of high conservation value tend to occur on the more infertile soils, and even where Bracken has been eradicated, recolonising species are frequently different to those of the original habitat. Loss or fragmentation of heathland by colonisation of Bracken results not only in loss of plants but of associated animals.

Gorse, often an indicator of enriched soils, is another invader of grazed heath. Island farmers burn Gorse patches regularly throughout the summer and early autumn - to control it and to provide new shoots for the animals to eat. In the past young shoots were cut for animal fodder.

V. Freshwater marsh

There is little open water in the islands. Lough Errul, at the western side of Cape Clear, which has a rather limited flora, is the largest. Lough Ordree on Sherkin is much smaller but has a good expanse of open water. The lough on East Calf has a well-developed aquatic flora and much open water.

Where open water occurs on the islands, it is usually fringed by reedbeds, dominated by Common Reed (*Phragmites australis*), and Grey Clubrush (*Scirpus lacustris* subsp.

tabernaemontani). These are well developed on Sherkin, notably at Tramore, at the eastern and western ends of Lough Ordree and in the pool behind the strand at Trabawn. The loughs on East Calf and towards the eastern end of Heir also have good reedbed vegetation. On Sherkin, bladderworts (*Utricularia*), their stems festooned with bladders with which they trap tiny animals, can be very abundant on the fringes of this habitat. Stoneworts, complex green algae, also occur in the open water of loughs and freshwater pools.

Polunin (unpublished notes) recorded that loughs and pools were used in those pre-machine days to wash clothes. Smith had noted two hundred years before how the people of Cape Clear washed linen in the soft water of Lough Errul.

Damp or wet, marshy ground is a feature of the islands, both by loughs and streams and in hollows of undrained pastures. Yellow Flag (*Iris pseudacorus*), a magnificent sight in early summer, dominates much of the marshy ground, together with Water Mint (*Mentha aquatica*), which gives this habitat a characteristic aromatic smell. Other plants include Common Fleabane (*Pulicaria dysenterica*), sometimes forming extensive yellow patches, Lesser Spearwort (*Ranunculus flammula*), Purple Loosetrife (*Lythrum salicaria*), with conspicuous reddish-purple spikes in late summer, and forget-me-nots. Overgrazed, wet pastures are dominated by rushes.

VI. Saltmarsh

There are only a few areas of saltmarsh. Most shorelines have a substrate of rock, shingle or sand rather than mud. Kinish Harbour, Sherkin, has some of the best-developed saltmarsh vegetation. Small patches of low, dense, saltmarsh sward have Common Saltmarsh-grass (*Puccinellia maritima*), Lax-flowered Sea-lavender (*Limonium humile*), Sea Arrowgrass (*Triglochin maritima*), Sea Aster (*Aster tripolium*) and Sea Plantain (*Plantago maritima*). Glasswort (*Salicornia europaea*) grows in open muddy patches. At the top of the marsh is a dense growth of Sea Rush (*Juncus maritimus*), with its sharp, spiky leaves.

A more characteristic type of saltmarsh vegetation is that which occurs on rocks by the sea, where grassland, heathland or even boggy communities grade into the salt-spray zone. Saltmarsh Rush (*Juncus gerardi*) and Sea Milkwort (*Glaux maritima*) form a lush growth, and Lesser Sea-spurrey (*Spergularia marina*) is often present. Slender Spike-rush (*Eleocharis uniglumis*) grows around brackish pools, sometimes with oraches and Red Goosefoot (*Chenopodium rubrum*).

A small area of sandy saltmarsh on the southern side of Heir has a sward dominated by Sea Hard-grass (*Parapholis strigosa*).

VII. Mires

Parts of the larger islands are covered with blanket bog, one of the characteristic habitats of western Ireland. The vegetation is dominated by bog-mosses (*Sphagnum*), Cross-leaved Heath (*Erica tetralix*) and Common Cotton-grass (*Eriophorum angustifolium*), with its distinctive 'cotton-wool' heads. Bog-mosses have a remarkable ability to absorb water and their dead, semi-decayed remains accumulate with other vegetable remains over long periods of time to form peat. Bog Asphodel (*Narthecium ossifragum*) and Round-leaved Sundew (*Drosera rotundifolia*) grow in wetter places. The sticky hairs on the reddish leaves of the sundew plant trap and digest insects, providing the plant with additional minerals in this nutrient-poor habitat. Drier peaty areas are dominated by Ling (*Calluna vulgaris*).

VIII. Freshwater

Open waters are described above under Freshwater Marsh. Running water, small streams and rills, is widespread on the larger islands. Streamside vegetation is often dominated by ferns, especially Lady Fern (*Athyrium filix-femina*), or a dense growth of tall flowering plants such as Meadow-sweet (*Filipendula ulmaria*). Ragged Robin (*Lychnis flos-cuculi*) and Lady's Smock (*Cardamine pratensis*) are characteristic plants of damp streamsides.

Where streams are wider, they are often choked with a dense mat of vegetation: Fool's Water-cress (*Apium nodiflorum*), water forget-me-nots (*Myosotis*) and starworts (*Callitriche*). Shallow, still, often muddy pools sometimes have a dense growth of water-crowfoots (*Ranunculus*). Blinks (*Montia fontana*) and Water-purslane (*Lythrum portula*), and also occasionally the bright, yellowish-green foliage of the Opposite-leaved Golden-saxifrage (*Chrysosplenium oppositifolium*), occur in the shallowest pools and in slow trickles of water or cart-ruts, together with a green scum of Duckweed (*Lemna minor*).

IX. Intertidal

The flora of the intertidal zones is dominated by seaweeds, the various marine algae. One genus of flowering plants, the eel-grasses (*Zostera*), has invaded this habitat, flowering and setting seed beneath the sea. Their long, strap-like leaves are often washed up on strands.

X. Coastal shingle

There are a number of small shingle strands in the islands. These carry an open vegetation of salt-tolerant beach plants and weeds such as Curled Dock (*Rumex crispus*). Where the shingle strands are more stable or extensive, especially with sand as well as stones, the vegetation becomes more closed and can be quite rich in species. The blue-grey foliage and yellow flowers of the Yellow-horned Poppy (*Glaucium flavum*), brighten the pebbles in late summer. The broad shingle strand at the western end of Long is one of the most interesting, with many plants, not least a large population of Little Robin (*Geranium purpureum*). Two other rare plants are restricted to this habitat: Sea Kale (*Crambe maritima*) and Sea Pea (*Lathyrus japonicus*). Shingle strands are also a refuge for arable weeds now that tillage is so restricted in the islands, for example, poppies (*Papaver*) are now seen more commonly at the tops of strands than on cultivated ground. Two members of the Mallow family are occasionally found on strands: Tree Mallow (*Lavatera arborea*) is more often associated with island gardens and Common Mallow (*Malva sylvestris*) is a plant of waysides.

XI. Sand-dunes (and sandy strands)

Sandy strands carry a flora of salt-tolerant, often fleshy plants. The most characteristic of these are Sea Purslane (*Honkenya peploides*), which forms a mass of stiff green shoots that turn yellow in autumn, fleshy-leaved oraches (*Atriplex*) and the grey, spiny Sea Holly (*Eryngium maritimum*). One of the most distinctive plants of strands and other sandy places near the shore is Sea Radish (*Raphanus raphanistrum* subsp. *maritimus*), abundant at several places in the islands.

There is little actively accreting blown sand in the islands. Where this occurs, the lowest dunes at the top of the beach build up around Sea Couch (*Elymus farctus*). The main sand-binding grass is Marram (*Ammophila arenaria*), forming characteristic coarse tussocks and patches. The plant can grow through several centimetres of sand, and the long, tough rhizomes bind the sand and prevent it from blowing away.

When the dune is stable it is invaded by other grasses and a rich grassland flora can develop on the shell-rich sand. These grasslands on blown sand are described above under Grasslands.

XII. Arable land

The weed flora of Roaringwater Bay is of national significance. Not only do some rare weeds such as Lesser Snapdragon (*Misopates orontium*) and Sharp-leaved Fluellen (*Kickxia elatine*) survive, but also the islands retain substantial fragments of weed *communities*. When Polunin was on Sherkin, he observed the traditional mixed agriculture of the islands: livestock, with fields of potatoes, oats, barley, rye, turnips, mangolds and fodder beet, cabbages and species-rich hayfields. Little large-scale tillage survives today - only garden vegetable plots. However, wherever somebody digs over a small area of cultivated land, or there is disturbance through building, weeds persist and sometimes flourish.

Several sites have yielded weeds during the last five years. Of particular interest during the 1990-5 was a cultivated plot to the south of the strand at Trabawn, Sherkin, overlooking the bay. The main crop was potatoes, with some carrots, turnips and fodder beet. The weed flora of the plot was dominated by Chickweed (*Stellaria media*) and Fat Hen (*Chenopodium album*). These two weeds are characteristic associates of root and cereal crops in Northern Europe, along with Common Sowthistle (*Sonchus oleraceus*), which was also present at Trabawn. Other weeds included Persicaria (*Persicaria maculosa*), Common Orache (*Atriplex patula*), Wild Turnip (*Brassia rapa* subsp. *campestris*), Charlock (*Sinapis arvensis*), Sun Spurge (*Euphorbia helioscopa*) and three fumitories (*Fumaria*).

A few oat plants, relics of former cultivation, were seen in most years. A field of oats at the western end of Heir supported substantial numbers of Field Pansy (*Viola arvensis*) and Field Woundwort (*Stachys arvensis*). These two weeds frequently occur together in the islands, notably on Cape Clear and Long, often with Corn Spurrey (*Spergula arvensis*).

Changes in land use, better seed cleaning and modern weed-killers have taken their toll of weeds. Recent resurveys of well-documented island floras show that many weeds have disappeared from other islands in the west, for example Inishbofin (Brodie & Sheehy Skeffington 1990) and Clare (Doyle & Foss 1986). Sherkin and Clear (and to a lesser extent other islands, notably Horse, Heir and Long) have, however, retained a substantial proportion of their weeds.

A different rich weed flora also persists on the Aran Islands in Galway Bay, especially on Inishmaan (Curtis *et al.* 1988). Fields have been built up carefully on top of bare limestone over many generations, using layers of seaweed and sand. Today, fields of rye used for hay and thatching allow the survival of three rare grasses - Darnel (*Lolium temulentum*), Smooth Brome (*Bromus racemosus*) and the ancient cultivated Bristle Oat (*Avena strigosa*) - together with Cornflower (*Centaurea cyanus*). (These four weeds have not been recorded from the islands of Roaringwater Bay, although Cornflower turned up on Cape Clear, in a batch of weeds introduced with wildflower seed, in 1995).

XIII. Waysides

The plants of disturbed places, roadsides and ruined buildings is of great interest. This *ruderal* or wayside flora is a mixture of weeds and plants introduced by people. Many of the plants are annuals or short-lived perennials and do not always persist for very long. Characteristic wayside plants in the islands are Musk Storksbill (*Erodium moschatum*) and, on Cape Clear, Sea Storksbill (*Erodium maritimum*). Many botanists, including the late Professor David Webb, have suggested that this flora has diminished in Ireland in recent years. However, the islands of Roaringwater Bay retain a substantial wayside flora. Many of these plants are discussed in the section above on Plants and People. One of the best places to see ruderals on Sherkin is in the area around the Castle. On Cape Clear, both North and South Harbours have a rich wayside flora. Heir too is a good place to seek out ruderal plants, especially along walls and by strands.

FLORA

Richness of the Flora

The flora of the islands is astonishingly rich. The islands are a mosaic of vegetation, much of it open and broken by rocky ground. The large proportion of coastline in the islands makes for a range of habitats: cliffs, rocks, sand and shingle strands. Salt and shell-rich beach sand vary the mostly acid nature of the soils. A long history of human occupation and cultivation has enriched the soil, created more habitats and introduced numerous plants.

The number of species recorded equals or exceeds that of any other part of Ireland. The islands of the West often have rich floras, but not nearly as rich as that of Roaringwater Bay. The table below shows the relative richness of Sherkin and Cape Clear as compared to two other islands of the coast of Western Ireland, Inishbofin (Brodie & Sheehy Skeffington 1990) and Clare (Doyle & Foss 1986). One of the reasons why the islands of Roaringwater Bay have a richer flora is that more plants of cultivated and disturbed ground have persisted.

Total number of flowering plants and ferns old figures and new surveys in 1985-95				
Island	Area (ha)	Highest Point (m)	No. plants (old count)	No. plants (1985-1995)
Sherkin	612	112	388 (1950)	483 (1995)
Cape Clear	658	159	373 (1973)	377 (1995)
Clare	1600	465	413 (1911)	329 (1986)
Inishbofin	930	88	367 (1968)	311 (1990)

The largest group of plants in Roaringwater Bay is the grasses (53 species). Sedges (23 species) are also important, as are ferns (20 species) and rushes (8 species).

Polunin and his students (unpublished notes) recorded a total of 413 species for the whole area, 388 of them on Sherkin. During the last 5 years we have confirmed that 592 different plants (including hybrids and subspecies) have been recorded in the islands since 1750.

The table overleaf gives the numbers of plants present today in each of the islands that we surveyed in Roaringwater Bay. The total number found in 1991-95 was 556.

A concentration of rare Irish plants

Ireland has few areas where rare plants are concentrated. This is in contrast to Britain, which possesses a more heterogeneous landscape and vegetation (Webb 1957). In Britain, certain special localities have long attracted botanists: Scotland's Ben Lawers and Glen Clova for their Arctic-Alpine floras, the Breckland of East Anglia for a group of steppe plants, and the Lizard peninsula in Cornwall for Mediterranean plants at the edge of their range. Webb (1957) provided an interesting map to show how rare Irish plants - those confined to not more than three places or to a small district - tend to occur mostly singly or in twos or threes.

Roaringwater Bay, alongside The Burren and the Galway Bay region, certainly can be described as an Irish botanical 'hotspot' like those of Britain. The islands of Roaringwater Bay, together with the adjacent Iveagh peninsula, are the Irish headquarters for Spotted Rockrose (*Tuberaria guttata*), Pale Heath Violet (*Viola lactea*) and, along with the Screen-Curracloe moraine of Co. Wexford (FitzGerald 1993), Bird's-foot (*Ornithopus perpusillus*) and Hairy Bird's Foot Trefoil (*Lotus subbiflorus*).

Total number of flowering plants and ferns (1985-1995)			
Sherkin	483	Horse	306
Cape Clear	377	Skeam W.	167
Bird	11	Skeam E.	227
Badger	27	Heir	381
W. Calf	178	Catalogues	148
M. Calf	221	Sandy	156
E. Calf	241	Quarantine	60
Carthys	67	Jeremy	68
Goat	74	Spanish	195
Little Goat	23	Inishleigh	141
Long	331	Mannin	142
Castle	228	**Total**	**556**

Twelve plants found in the islands of Roaringwater Bay are included in the Irish Red Data Book (Curtis & McGough 1988). These are: Bird's-foot, Hairy Bird's-foot Trefoil, Lanceolate Spleenwort (*Asplenium obovatum* subsp. *lanceolatum*), Lesser Snapdragon (*Misopates orontium*), Pale Dog-violet, Little Robin (*Geranium purpureum*), Sea Kale (*Crambe maritima*), Sea Pea (*Lathyrus japonicus*), Slender Centaury (*Centaurium pulchellum*), Sharp-leaved Fluellen (*Kickxia elatine*) and Spotted Rockrose. Corn Cockle (*Agrostemma githago*) is now extinct. Two other plants, Deptford Pink (*Dianthus armeria*) and Fiddle Dock (*Rumex pulcher*) ought to be included in any future edition of the Irish Red Data Book.

Other nationally rare or very local plants on the islands include Babington's Leek (*Allium ampeloprasum* var. *babingtonii*), Dotted Sedge (*Carex punctata*), Elecampane (*Inula helenium*), Field Woundwort (*Stachys arvensis*), Good King Henry (*Chenopodium bonus-henricus*), Grey Sedge (*Carex divulsa*), Henbit Dead-nettle (*Lamium amplexicaule*), Knotted Hedge-parsley (*Torilis nodosa*), Marsh Mallow (*Althaea officinalis*), Musk Storksbill (*Erodium moschatum*), Purple Ramping-fumitory (*Fumaria purpurea*), Red Campion (*Silene dioica*), Sea Storksbill (*Erodium maritimum*), Small-fruited Prickly-sedge (*Carex muricata*), Wild Celery (*Apium graveolens*), Wild Madder (*Rubia peregrina*), Wormwood (*Artemisia absinthium*), Yellow Centaury (*Cicendia filiformis*) and a group of clovers, otherwise mostly south-eastern in distribution in Ireland, including Bird's-foot Clover (*Trifolium ornithopodioides*), Hare's-foot Clover (*T. arvense*), Knotted Clover (*T. striatum*) and Slender Trefoil (*T. micranthum*).

This makes a total of **at least 30 rare plants on the islands**, an astonishing figure for so small an area. The protection of their habitats, which include other interesting or local species, is clearly of vital importance within the national strategy for the protection of threatened plants in Ireland. Many of these rare plants are protected under the provisions of the Flora Protection Order 1987. The wild plants of the islands are vulnerable and precious, and should not be picked, and certainly not uprooted. **Please leave wild flowers for others to enjoy.**

There are a few rare plants on the adjacent mainland which are not known to occur on the islands. These include three more Red Data Book plants. Green-winged Orchid (*Orchis morio*), rare and scattered in Ireland, has its only West Cork stations at Barley Cove, from where it had first been reported by R.W. Townsend in the mid-19th Century (Power 1845), and Rock Island near Goleen (O'Mahony 1995). Three-lobed Crowfoot (*Ranunculus tripartitus*) occurs near Adrigole and was also reported from south of Baltimore by Phillips. It was recently reported at three other Irish stations in Kerry (Curtis & Harrington 1987). Wild Clary (*Salvia horminoides*), a very local plant of southern and eastern coastal counties, with a few isolated stations in the west, has long been recorded from the castle mound at Baltimore.

Other rare plants are found on the Iveagh peninsula. Prostrate Broom (*Cytisus scoparius* subsp. *prostratus*) is found at Three Castles Head and Strawberry Tree or Arbutus (*Arbutus unedo*) survives on rocks near Crookhaven and on Mount Gabriel. Spotted Rockrose, the speciality of the islands of Roaringwater Bay, occurs at Sheeps Head, Three Castles Head and near Crookhaven, and the Iveagh peninsula also has populations of Bird's-foot and Hairy Bird's-foot Trefoil, which both have their West Cork distribution centred on Cape Clear, Sherkin and other islands. The whole region of Roaringwater Bay is thus quite incredibly rich in rare Irish plants.

Most of the rare plants of the islands are either heathland species or weeds of cultivation. In other words they are all plants of open ground rather than of bogs, grassland or woodland. Overall, Ireland lacks the open, often sandy habitats of Britain. This is reflected in the distribution of even common species. Sand Spurrey (*Spergularia rubra*), recorded from Cape Clear and the nearby mainland, is very local in Ireland, but widespread in Britain on the open ground of sandy heaths. Similarly, Buckshorn Plantain (*Plantago coronopus*) is almost always coastal in Ireland, whereas in Britain it occurs inland, again on open, sandy ground. The areas of open, rocky ground on the islands provide favourable conditions for the survival of many plants of open habitats.

The broken, rocky nature of the terrain has been described above under Geology. This is a favoured habitat for several of the rarer plants. The thin soils dry out during summer, thus preventing encroachment by more vigorous species and allowing the plants themselves to die down and the seeds to ripen. Most of this group of plants are annuals more characteristic of southern Europe and the Mediterranean region: the clovers, Bird's-foot and Hairy Bird's-foot Trefoil, and Spotted Rockrose.

The glacial and post-glacial history of the region has had much bearing on the present flora. Even more so than in Britain, arctic conditions and the physical action of moving ice-sheets (centred on the mountains of Munster) caused massive destruction of the existing flora and vegetation. Soils too were destroyed and much of the soil that has developed since has been peaty rather than brown earths or other more mineral-rich soils.

It is possible that a few sites in western Ireland remained ice-free on the periphery of the glaciers. Such sites, known as nunataks, may have been refugia for certain plants such as Spotted Rockrose. The present distribution of this plant in Ireland, restricted to a few promonteries and islands of West Cork, Connemara and (Inishturk) West Mayo, supports this view. (It also occurs on the west coast of Anglesey and nearby Lleyn peninsula in Wales.)

BOTANICAL EXPLORATION OF THE ISLANDS

Historical outline

The first botanist to record plants in the islands was James Drummond (1784-1863), as a young man the Curator of the Cork Botanic Garden. He was an able botanist who is best known for having added Large-flowered Butterwort (*Pinguicula grandiflora*) and Irish Lady's-tresses (*Spiranthes romanzoffiana*) to the Irish flora. He made several significant records in the Cork flora during the period 1800-1820, which he published in the *Munster Farmer's Magazine*, 6-7: 21,23,25 & 26 (1818-20). Sadly for Irish botany, he subsequently emigrated to Australia, where he became Colonial Botanist to the Swann River settlement (modern Perth).

Many early records come from Revd Thomas Allin (d.1909), for some time curate in Midleton, East Cork. He then moved to England, to Weston-super-Mare in Somerset, where he published a slim but most useful Flora of Co. Cork (Allin 1883). This contains new species and distributional records for the county, many of which were incorporated into *Cybele Hibernica* (Colgan & Scully 1898). Allin also published short notes in *Journal of Botany*, a London-based periodical, during the years 1871-4. He was based for a time in West Cork and visited several of the islands in Roaringwater Bay, making important records on West and East Calf and on Sherkin (Inisherkin). Records from the islands published in his *Flora* are noted below in the Systematic Section of the text.

The most significant plant recorder in this area from the late 19th Century was Robert Albert Phillips (1866-1945), a commercial traveller for Guys of Cork. He recorded all over Co. Cork, contributing plant records to Robert Lloyd Praeger's *Irish Topographic Botany* (Praeger 1901). However, his job enabled him to spend more of his time recording outside his native county, notably around Limerick in 1904-5. He made an immense contribution to Irish botany, being the first to find, amongst other plants, Pale Dog-Violet (*Viola lactea*) in Ireland. Sherkin remains one of the Irish strongholds of this rare plant.

Some 90% of Phillips' West Cork records in Praeger (1901) were made in 1896, many of them from the Skibbereen area and from Roaringwater Bay. From that year on he was busy in Roaringwater Bay and we are fortunate that his own, annotated copy of Allin's *Flora* found its way into the hands of Desmond Meikle, a distinguished Irish botanist who formerly worked at the Royal Botanic Gardens, Kew. This volume, which Meikle has donated to the library of the National Herbarium, Glasnevin, Dublin, includes a number of important records added in pencil by Phillips, such as Fiddle Dock (*Rumex pulcher*) on Sherkin and Lanceolate Spleenwort (*Asplenium obovatum* subsp. *lanceolatum*) on Cape Clear. Many but by no means all of these records were summarised in Colgan & Scully (1898) and Praeger (1901).

There is then a gap of some 40 years. Robert Lloyd Praeger (1865-1953), giant amongst Irish botanists and naturalists, covered most of Ireland, but does not seem to have recorded much in Roaringwater Bay. He obviously appreciated the other charms of this place, for he wrote in *The Way that I went* (Praeger 1936): "You stay on Sherkin Island ... or Cape Clear Island ... and you walk and boat and fish and lounge and bathe, and enjoy the glorious air and sea". Clearly Roaringwater Bay was where this legendary naturalist relaxed with his family! In *The Botanist in Ireland* (Praeger 1934), he mentions Spotted Rock-rose on "the Calf Islands" and nearby Three Castles Head on the mainland and quotes some of Phillips' work, but that is all.

The first major inventory of the flora of Sherkin and the other islands was that of Oleg Vladimirovich Polunin (1914-1985). A schoolmaster by profession, Polunin had a wide knowledge of plants and his subsequent work took him all over Europe and as far as the Middle East, the Caucasus and the Himalayas (Akeroyd 1986). He visited Sherkin in the summers of 1948-51, only a few years after Phillips' death. Polunin's work on the flora and vegetation of Sherkin and the other islands laid the foundations for all subsequent studies. This recording, together with the 10-km square centred on Godalming, Surrey, that he worked over for the Botanical Society of the British Isles' *Atlas of the British Flora* (Perring & Walters 1962), was his major contribution to the study of the flora of Britain and Ireland.

Each summer during this period he would stay for an extended period at Lough Hyne or Sherkin with his family and some of his pupils from Charterhouse School, Surrey, and their friends. Polunin rediscovered several of the important finds of Phillips, although he was unable to relocate other 19th Century stations for rare plants. Indeed, these did not turn up again until the intensive studies of the 1990s. Polunin submitted a full catalogue of his finds to *Watsonia*, the then new journal of the Botanical Society of the British Isles (Polunin 1949), but this was apparantly heavily edited and only the most significant finds were published in a rather dry account a year later (Polunin 1950). It is amusing and a bit sad to see that Corn Cockle (*Agrostemma githago*), fast disappearing in Ireland at that time and now extinct, was not thought by the editors to be worthy of comment in the final paper. Conservation was not very widely accepted in those days. A copy of Polunin's valuable unpublished draft, now in the archives of the Sherkin Island Marine Station, is appended to this Flora (Appendix 1).

During the 1950s the islands of Roaringwater Bay continued to attract botanists from Ireland and Britain. The most notable of them was J. Emmet O'Donovan, of Union Hall, West Cork, who added Hairy Bird's-foot Trefoil to the flora of Ireland, from Cape Clear, and Bird's-foot Clover to the flora of West Cork, from the pier at Baltimore and from North Harbour, Cape Clear. He also published a useful floristic paper with the ornithologist and archaeologist Bernard O'Regan (O'Donovan & O'Regan 1952). O'Regan died as recently as 1995, aged 98.

Another botanist working here during this period was Mrs Mary C.D. Bridges, one of the Townsends of Castletownsend, West Cork. Her forbears, R.W. Townsend and his daughter Harriet Townsend, were also keen botanists; Harriet had added Spotted Rockrose to the Irish flora from Three Castles Head, West Cork, prior to 1843. Later found by Phillips on East Calf and Heir, and by botanists from Sherkin Island Marine Station on Long, this plant is now regarded as the greatest floral treasure of Roaringwater Bay. Mrs Bridges corresponded with Maura Scannell in the National Herbarium during the 1960s and 1970s.

In 1975, Matt and Eileen Murphy founded Sherkin Island Marine Station. In the same year, Pat Whelan, with Pat McCarthy and Sister Martin Powell, produced an updated provisional inventory of the flora, with lists of plants from the various islands, whilst working at the Station. They made several important records, notably the rediscovery after some 25 years of Knotted Hedge-parsley (*Torilis nodosa*) on Horse. Tony O'Mahony, currently (with Maura Scannell) the Botanical Society of the British Isles' plant recorder for Co. Cork, visited Sherkin briefly in 1976 and 1977, adding Soft Clover (*Trifolium striatum*) to the flora, a very rare plant in Co. Cork and indeed in Ireland. He returned to the islands in 1993, when he added several new records including the attractive pink-flowered subspecies of Hedge Bindweed (*Calystegia sepium* subsp. *roseata*).

The extensive work of the young British botanist Lucy Wright in 1981-82 is reported below. The Station attracted other botanists from Ireland and Britain. In 1981 a party from the University of Southampton led by Frank Bisby stayed on Sherkin; duplicates of their collections of vetches and clovers, collected as part of work on an international legume data-base (ILDIS), are in the herbarium on Sherkin. A visitor during the 1970s and 1980s was Maura Scannell, indefatigable Curator of the National Herbarium at Glasnevin who has done so much to encourage and coordinate recording, especially by younger botanists, in Ireland.

In 1986 three English botanists from the University of Reading Herbarium visited Sherkin. Mrs Carol Hora had corresponded with Matt Murphy over the sale of books from the library of her late husband, F. Bayard Hora, celebrated mycologist and lecturer at Reading. Her business correspondence with Matt grew into friendship and she was keen to visit Sherkin and Sherkin Island Marine Station. She was accompanied by her younger colleagues John Robert Akeroyd and Stephen Leonard Jury, who, impressed both by the flora and by the recording work, resolved to continue botanical research on Sherkin. Both had extensive field experience in Ireland, with a special interest in plants of more southern or Mediterranean distribution. Stephen Jury helped set up the Station's moss and lichen herbarium.

John Akeroyd was back on Sherkin in July 1987, with David Allardice Webb (1913-1994, Professor of Botany at Trinity College, Dublin, and an old friend of Oleg Polunin). They visited Sherkin, Ringarogy and the adjacent mainland around Baltimore, as part of the BSBI's 'Monitoring Scheme' to assess changes to the British and Irish floras since the *Atlas of the British Flora* was published in 1962. John Akeroyd returned, visiting Sherkin, Cape Clear and most of the other islands with the Station's young botanists, in 1990 and 1992-95. He and they contributed new records and gradually tracked down most of Phillips' and Polunin's finds: his most interesting discovery was Fiddle Dock (*Rumex pulcher*) on Sherkin after a gap of nearly 100 years.

In June 1992, the Botanical Society of the British Isles held a meeting on Sherkin. The party met up with Karen Clarke (see below), whose records and rediscoveries of rare plants had generated considerable outside interest in Sherkin's flora. At the end of that eventful summer, the discovery of Deptford Pink (*Dianthus armeria*), a species and genus never before reported as truly wild in Ireland, during a cold, wet afternoon's excursion on Horse, caused a distinct ripple of excitement amongst British and Irish botanists. Suddenly a lot of people were talking about the flora of Sherkin and Roaringwater Bay. It became imperative to compile the Flora before others stole the glory from the young botanists who had made most of the discoveries.

The contribution of the Sherkin Island Marine Station botanists

It was clear by the end of 1992 that Roaringwater Bay was an area as rich as the Burren or any other locality in Ireland. Amongst all this excitement, however, one must not forget that science involves hard, patient work over a long period. The *major* contribution to the study of the flora has been made by the young botanists who have worked at the Marine Station. Seven individuals - **Lucy Wright, Jennifer Shockley, Karen Clarke, Nick Rowe, Pat Hatch, Mike Robinson** and **Beth Milner** - have made the largest contribution.

The solid foundations for the present Flora were laid by **Lucy Wright**, who was on Sherkin in the autumn of 1981 and for much of 1982. Her meticulous surveys of the vegetation, her species lists and herbarium are the basis of all the work that followed. Her single most important plant discovery was Slender Centaury (*Centaurium pulchellum*) on Horse, its first confirmed record in Co. Cork since Drummond had found it in 1818!

In 1990, **Jennifer Shockley** from America prepared a detailed checklist which has provided a reliable basis and skeleton for the systematic section of this present Flora. In 1992, another American botanist, **Karen Clarke**, with experience in surveys of rare species, tracked down several of the rarer plants, adding new records and rediscovering amongst other remarkable finds, Spotted Rock-rose on East Calf, a record alluded to by Praeger but not confirmed until 1992! She added Babington's Leek (*Allium ampeloprasum* var. *babingtonii*) to the flora of Sherkin, the most significant extension to its recorded range for over a century.

This work was consolidated in 1993 by **Nick Rowe**, from England, who diligently tracked down both common and rare plants and filled in gaps in known distributions, notably in difficult groups such as sedges, rushes and aquatics. He discovered Little Robin (*Geranium purpureum*) on Long, a plant known otherwise in Ireland from just a few stations about Cork City. During the next two years, three English botanists, **Pat Hatch** and **Mike Robinson** (1994), and **Beth Milner** (1995) added or confirmed many important records, especially on Long, Horse and Heir. Good finds in 1994 included Sea Kale (*Crambe maritima*) on Middle Calf, also new stations for Spotted Rock-rose, Lanceolate Spleenwort and Sharp-leaved Fluellen (*Kickxia elatine*). Significant discoveries in 1995 were Sea Pea (*Lathyrus japonicus*) on Castle and Heir, hybrids and sedges, and several plants not seen since Oleg Polunin's visits. By the end of the 1995 recording season, Marine Station botanists had confirmed almost all the finds of Allin, Phillips and Polunin.

It is interesting to note that this body of work was carried out by young botanists outside the academic establishment of Ireland and Britain. *The work presented in this Flora is thus almost entirely that of botanists and associated research workers of the Sherkin Island Marine Station, building on the firm foundation laid by Oleg Polunin.*

BRIEF DESCRIPTION OF THE ISLANDS

Every island has its own character and distinctive flora and vegetation. In this section we outline features of each island or group for the benefit of the visitor. Living and working on Sherkin we have had the privilege of exploring throughout the islands. Most visitors will be there for just a short period, perhaps only one or two days, even just a few hours. This brief guide sets the scene and is a basis for further exploration.

Sherkin

Sherkin has all the habitats present in the islands. It also has the largest flora. Obviously it has received more attention from Marine Station botanists - even the walk to the post office or one of the two pubs has yielded several new finds! Nonetheless, it is more sheltered than the other islands and exhibits a wide range of topography and land use.

Sherkin, 10 minutes from Baltimore by ferry, is easily explored by the visitor. A tarmac road leads from the ferry landing-stage at Abbey Strand to the south western end of the island. Another road runs from the Abbey, past the Castle, Murphy's Bar and the Jolly Roger, to The Dock at the north-eastern corner of the island. Just to the west of Kinish Harbour the main east-west road forks and another good road runs to Cow and Silver Strands, with their fine sands and safe bathing. A network of footpaths and tracks enable the visitor to reach the western coast, Horseshoe Harbour and the lighthouse, but much of Slievemore, including the bay of Foardree, and the peninsula of Farranacoush are difficult of access.

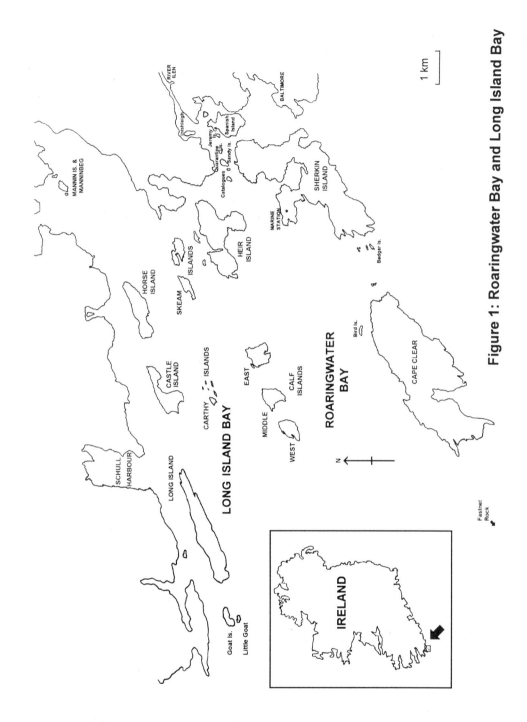

Figure 1: Roaringwater Bay and Long Island Bay

The island rises to 112 m on its hilly backbone, Slievemore. The walk up - the summit is best approached from the south side - provides an opportunity to see interesting heathland plants and the high ground affords magnificent views across to Cape Clear and is a good place to watch for whales, porpoises and dolphins. In a valley on the north side lies Lough Ordree, fringed by an extensive reedswamp and marshes. These contain Bulrushes, the imposing Royal Fern and a rich sedge flora, which includes Bottle, Cyperus, Greater Pond and Greater Tussock sedges. Care should be taken for it is a deep and dangerous lake and drownings do occur.

Much of the island is rough grazing and heathland, with some woodland and scrub developing. The main grazing animals on the island today are cattle; there are no rabbits. The settlement at the eastern end has most of the island's facilities and the majority of the inhabitants live between the harbour and Trabawn. The population stands at about 90, which increases substantially during the summer months.

The coastal heathlands are best seen at the beautiful bays of Horseshoe Harbour and Trabawn. Horseshoe Harbour has several rare clovers and other plants, while Trabawn has a range of vegetation that includes very fine coastal heathland. The marsh at Trabawn has many wetland plants and the adjacent strand and low cliffs are species-rich. The low sward of the promontory on the northern side of the bay is a carpet of miniature flowers in summer. The pastures on the south-eastern side of the bay are bright with orchids and other grassland flowers.

The south side of Kinish Harbour has saltmarsh communities and the only substantial stand of woodland in the islands. Two climbing plants on walls are a feature: the vine-like Hop and the coastal subspecies of Hedge Bindweed, with pink-striped trumpet flowers. A relatively short walk along the northern branch of the road takes one to Cow and Silver Strands. Here the grassland on blown sand is a mass of orchids and other flowers in June. In late August, Autumn Lady's-tresses flowers freely by rock outcrops above the strand. Hop Trefoil grows on a wall near Cow Strand at its main locality in the islands. Another distinctive plant here is Sea Radish, abundant on the sandy roadside.

The stone walls and sheltered lanes of Sherkin have a varied flora, especially of ferns. The base of walls along the road to the Dock is a good place to see a range of ferns, especially Hay-scented Buckler-fern, Hard Fern and Soft Shield-fern. The settlement at the eastern end has many interesting plants associated with the long human occupation of the island. The Castle has a rich flora of weeds and ancient medicinal plants, including the stately Elecampane and Alexanders. By nearby cottages grow Hemlock and Wormwood.

Many of the cottages have neat and attractive gardens, and the Fuchsia hedges, covered with thousands of pendulous red flowers, are magnificent all through the summer.

Cape Clear

The largest and most hilly (up to 159 m) of the islands, Cape Clear has substantial areas of higher ground, much of it covered by heathland and farmland. The 130 or so inhabitants earn their living by farming, fishing and tourism. Cape Clear is Irish-speaking and a centre for the study of the Irish language and traditional culture. The island has a network of tarmac roads with a surprising amount of motor traffic.

Trees are few on this exposed island, but there are some shelter belts and many hedges. Pastures are grazed by cattle, and a few goats, and there is a large population of rabbits. There are extensive haymeadows on the island, but all appear to have been improved by reseeding and the application of fertilizers.

Wetlands are concentrated at the western end. As well as Lough Errul, the major water body in the islands, there are West Bog, Central Bog (drained in the 1960s) and East Bog. East Bog is the largest and is dominated by reed swamp. Smaller communities of damp- or wet-loving

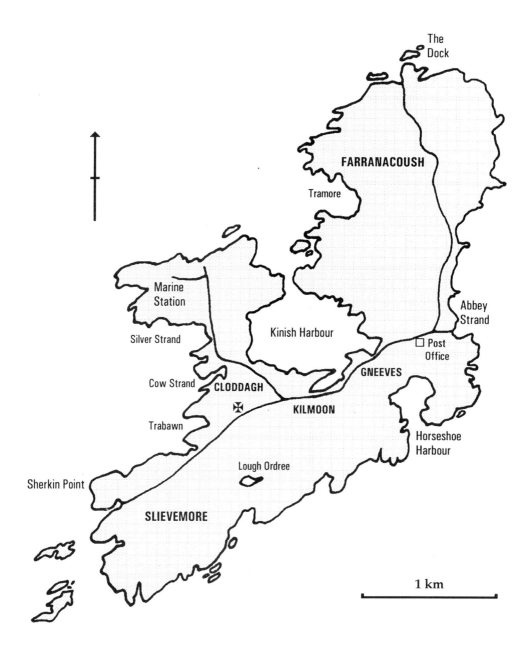

Figure 2: Sherkin Island

plants, including luxuriant ferns, are found along small streams and runnels. Drystone walls provide another fern habitat, notably for the lime- and frost-intolerant Lanceolate Spleenwort and Hay-scented Buckler-fern.

Lough Errul has a relatively poor flora apart from large populations of two plants. The southern, and to a lesser extent the eastern, margin is coloured pink in late summer by a dense stand of Amphibious Bistort. Much of the stony bottom of the lake is covered by a dense mat of Shoreweed, only seen when the water level is lower as in the dry summer of 1995. The waysides and Bracken-covered banks between Lough Errul and South Harbour have a number of interesting plants, including Marsh Mallow and Red Campion - Cape Clear is the only island in the Bay where the latter occurs.

Cape Clear is mostly bounded with steep cliffs and precipitous rocks, so sand and shingle strands are poorly developed, as is saltmarsh. The steep slopes above South Harbour have some of the best dry coastal heathland in the islands; Hairy Bird's-foot Trefoil grows here in the site where it was first discovered in Ireland by J. Emmet O'Donovan and others in 1953.

Hardly any tillage remains. Crops of Turnip Rape at the western end of the island are rich in weeds. One field in 1992 had both a golden carpet of Corn Marigold and a few plants of the very rare Henbit Dead-nettle. However, in 1993-95 it was under grass. Records held at the Bird Observatory show that Lesser Snapdragon has come up repeatedly over 30 years in fields near South Harbour. Note that access can be difficult and permission should always be sought from landowners.

Recent building above South Harbour has created open disturbed habitats suitable for weeds. Sowing of commercial wildflower seed in 1995 has confused the picture, but several arable weeds have come up in this area in the last five years, presumably from buried seed. North Harbour is a good place to look for weeds and one rare plant at least, Bird's-foot Clover, survives amongst the cobbles of the harbour moles. Musk Storksbill is often frequent on waysides near the Bird Observatory, and can be found on walls right across to South Harbour. With it is the diminutive Sea Storksbill, a speciality of the Cape Clear flora. The top of the wall outside the Youth Hostel at South Harbour is a good place to see these two storksbills!

The Calfs

West, Middle and East Calf form a chain in the very centre of Roaringwater Bay. From higher ground on Cape Clear on a sunny day they are a striking sight, dark patches in a blue sea and remarkably low-lying. West Calf rises to 22 m, Middle Calf to just 11 m and East Calf to 19 m. They are consequently exposed and treeless. Nevertheless, all were settled and the last inhabitants left only in the 1940s. Today, cattle are still grazed amongst the ruins of the former farms. Hares occur on all three islands.

West Calf is less grazed and is dominated by rank grassland. West and Middle Calf have small areas of blown sand and Middle and East Calf have shingle strands. Middle Calf has marshy ground and a series of broad shingle strands at the western end. The strands have a classic seaside flora, including Yellow-horned Poppy, Sea Spurge, Sea Kale and Sea-holly. East Calf has more habitat diversity, with heathland on higher ground (including a famous locality for Spotted Rockrose), grassland over blown sand and a small lough surrounded by marshy ground rich in plants. The lough has yielded numerous records of aquatic plants, including pondweeds and water-crowfoots.

The Carthys

The Carthys are four low, rocky islands, very exposed and home to large numbers of sea-birds, mainly gulls. These damage the vegetation by trampling and over-enrichment by their droppings. North Island has in the past been grazed by sheep. There is some shingle and coastal grassland, but the flora is mostly plants of the salt-spray zone and common weeds, including stands of Hogweed and thistles. The only plant of note is Sea Radish, which is abundant.

Goat & Little Goat

Goat, surrounded by rugged cliffs, rises steeply to 32 m. The vegetation is heathland dominated by rank grasses and some gorse. The few plants recorded grow mostly on rock outcrops. There are traces of a former farm or croft, around which the soil is deeper and presumably improved.

Little Goat is an adjacent sea-stack with very few flowering plants recorded. Both Goat and Little Goat are difficult to reach and to explore, and of more interest for their birds (best seen from a boat) than their plants!

Long

This is the largest island after Cape Clear and Sherkin. However, it is low-lying, with a maximum elevation of 29 m. There are 20 permanent inhabitants, most of whom live on the northern side of the central part of the island. A good track runs for much of the length of the island, but fades into a path at the eastern end. The island is almost treeless. Heathland dominates, with some areas of pasture. There is boggy ground, with peaty pools that support a rich aquatic flora. Sheep and cattle graze enclosed areas of heathland at the eastern end of the island.

Stone walls, especially along tracks, are rich in plants and in one place at least, the rare fern, Lanceolate Spleenwort. A wall at the settlement towards the western end has a thriving population of the rare geranium Little Robin, known elsewhere in Ireland only from Cork City. Several of the gardens on Long have interesting collections of plants, some of which have escaped. These include medicinal plants and herbs, such as mints, Horse-radish and Comfrey.

The shingle and coastal grassland towards the western end has a rich flora including Little Robin, Yellow Horned-poppy and various uncommon weeds.

Castle

Castle, rising to 36 m, is dominated by gorse scrub and bracken, with occasional willows and improved pastures grazed by sheep. There are ruined settlements at the eastern end and to the west of the tower (ruins of an O'Mahony castle). Wayside weeds, such as Good King Henry, Small Nettle and Musk Storksbill are relics of former human occupation and disturbance. A shingle strand south of the castle has a number of seaside plants, including a low-growing variant of Herb Robert.

The cliffs towards the eastern end are dissected by ivy-covered gullies and have a lush vegetation of tall plants, such as Royal Fern and Irish Spurge. Heathland occurs on the rising ground at the western end of the island.

Horse

Horse is a low-lying island with a maximum elevation of 37 m. A stony track leads from the old village at the eastern end to the landing stage at the north-western corner. Much of the island is overgrown by scrub and bracken (the home, it should be noted, of numerous ticks), but the track is a convenient way to reach the most interesting habitats.

The soil of much of the island is clayey, damp and frequently water-logged. Willows grow well in the damp soil and are a feature of Horse, with several species and hybrids apparently introduced. Recently other trees have been planted, including Aspen and Birch, together with garden plants such as Tree Mallow and Pampas Grass. Sheep graze parts of the island, but goats were removed in 1994.

There are also some fine coastal grasslands dominated by blown sand at the western end. At the eastern end, rock outcrops alternate with some of the most interesting grasslands in the islands. Copper and small amounts of other minerals used to be mined in this area and the overgrown spoil heaps and adjacent grassland carry a special flora that includes at least two colonies of Common Broomrape, and Deptford Pink at its only known Irish station. Nearby in 1995 grew the largest group of Great Mullein to be seen in the islands. These imposing plants, up to 2 m tall, dominated an old trackway.

A large house at the western end of Horse is lived in from time to time and one of the old dwellings of the eastern settlement has been refurbished. At least three more houses are being erected at the present time, presumably as holiday cottages. This has not apparently damaged the most important habitats and, indeed, has allowed dormant weed seed to germinate, including that of some of the rarer weeds like Purple Ramping-fumitory and Sharp-leaved Fluellen.

The Skeams

These two islands are very different in character. Skeam West is for the most part a west-east valley flanked by rocky, heathy ground. The valley has lush grassland. At the western end there is a shingle beach. The small settlement at the eastern end has been restored as a holiday property but remains deserted. Knotted Hedge-parsley grows here, together with other weeds and plants of disturbed ground. The church by the settlement is said to date from the 9th Century. Sheep are grazed from time to time on this treeless island.

Skeam East has a more varied topography including an impressive rock arch on the western coast. Heathland dominates the higher, rocky ground and pasture, which is grazed by goats and cattle, covers the lower, damper, sometimes marshy ground. A few planted conifers persist, but the island is mostly treeless. The ruins of a small settlement by the strand at the eastern end have an interesting weed flora. The strand is a traditional landing place for livestock and nearby grow Small Nettle, Wormwood and other weeds of local distribution in the islands. Pellitory-of-the-Wall, growing on the ruins, is a probably relic of former medicinal use by the inhabitants.

Heir (Hare)

Apart from Sherkin and Cape Clear, Heir has the largest number of flowering plants and ferns in the islands. The island is mostly low-lying, with the highest ground (up to 92 m) at the western end. The island has 10 inhabitants, but more visitors come in summer (the island supports both a small village shop and a restaurant!). A road runs from the East Pier almost the length of the island, becoming a track and eventually a path. Houses are scattered, mostly at the eastern end and towards the west near the large inlet - which is spanned by a sturdy causeway.

Most of the island is covered by species-poor pastures that are grazed by cattle. The most interesting and significant habitat is heathland, which dominates the western end of Heir. The most westerly part is a coastal heath surrounded by cliffs and almost cut off from the rest of the island by a deep inlet. Heathy ridges, following the SW-NE direction of the rock strata, extend eastwards from here.

In the central part of the island, south of the old school, is an extensive marsh, dominated by a reed bed. The damp ground near the sea has a conspicuous stand of Parsley Water Dropwort in summer. The main inlet towards the western end has some saltmarsh on its margins and there is an interesting sandy saltmarsh in the south-eastern corner of the island. Nearby strands have fine growths of Sea Radish, Wormwood and the oraches that are so characteristic of strand vegetation.

The deserted school house on Heir is a notable site for ferns. Several occur in abundance on the walls of the old playground; of special interest is Rusty-back Fern at its main station in Roaringwater Bay, and Wall Spleenwort at its only station in the islands. Both benefit from the lime-rich mortar of the wall.

A few gardens, potato patches and areas of disturbed ground have arable weeds. These include fine stands of fumitories, Corn Spurrey, Field Pansy, Field Woundwort, Black Bindweed, Pale Persicaria and, apparently a more recent arrival, Ivy-leaved Speedwell. Two-rowed Barley in one place is a relic of former cultivation.

The choicest plant on Heir is Spotted Rockrose, which flourishes in at least two heathy places. Should you find this delicate plant, leave it for others to enjoy. It has survived here probably since the glaciers retreated and it would be sad for us to lose it now. It is very inconspicuous and the flowers are mostly fallen by the time summer visitors arrive.

Catalogues, Sandy, Quarantine and Jeremy

This group of small islands lies between Sherkin and Spanish. They have remarkably rich and varied floras, reflecting both a range of habitats and episodes of human disturbance. Each is different and distinctive: the Catalogues (a group of five small islands) and Sandy have heathy grassland, Quarantine has a small saltmarsh on the eastern side, Jeremy is rocky. Even the smaller of the islands have fragments of the plant communities of the larger islands and mainland - for example, Angelica on Quarantine, Purple Moor-grass on Jeremy and numerous sedges on Sandy.

Spanish

Spanish lies at the eastern end of the Bay, near the mainland, rising to 32 m. The vegetation of Spanish is similar to that of the adjacent mainland. The island has extensive scrub, dominated by Gorse and Blackthorn, and hedges, with several small trees: Ash, Hazel, Holly, Oak and Sycamore. The east side, especially around the ruined settlement is very overgrown. Woodland plants such as Barren Strawberry, Enchanter's-nightshade, Wood-sorrel, Wood Avens and Yellow Pimpernel flourish in the shade of the scrub and Bracken.

Heathland occupies the higher ground, grading into areas of blanket bog. There is a mosaic of communities: Purple Moor-grass dominates the drier areas whereas wetter ground is covered with hummocks of bog-moss. On the coasts, which are muddy on the eastern side, there are some small saltmarshes

Inishleigh

Inishleigh is dominated by overgrazed pasture, with heath and coastal grassland at the western end. At the northern end of the island there is saltmarsh and a shingle strand. The island is grazed by cattle which cross over from the mainland at low tide.

Mannin (and Mannin Beg)

Mannin, grazed by sheep, is mostly low-lying, and rises to just 20 m. Heathland covers most of the southern part of the island, with some coastal grassland and marshy ground. The northern half is overgrown with Bracken, but a few remnant trees remain near the ruins of a former settlement. There are a few small areas of saltmarsh, particularly on Mannin Beg.

SYSTEMATIC LIST OF THE FLORA

Notes on the List

This account has been compiled from records assembled between 1975 and 1995, from historical books and papers, from cumulative field research by botanists based at Sherkin Island Marine Station and by the gleaning of notes and observations from other botanists. Some of those who contributed were able to return repeatedly to the islands, others had extended stays; some of us could only manage the occasional short visit. Little field work was done during early spring, so the observations have a summer to autumn seasonal bias. Many years of work by many different people at the Marine Station - American, British and Irish - have gone into what we present here. This is by no means the last word and we hope that readers will be able to fill in some of the gaps that we have, by necessity, left in this inventory.

The islands in Roaringwater Bay are listed in the order:

Sherkin, Cape Clear, Bird, Badger, the Calfs (W, M & E), Carthys, Goat, Little Goat, Long, Castle, Horse, the Skeams (W & E), Heir, Catalogues, Sandy, Quarantine, Jeremy, Spanish, Inishleigh and Mannin (including Mannin Beg). We have also included some records from the adjacent mainland, especially in and around Baltimore, the main port serving the islands and the base for the ferry to Sherkin. As the plant life of Roaringwater Bay is so rich, the Flora should also serve as a useful list for much of West Cork.

The order of species follows the most recent edition of *Census Catalogue of the Flora of Ireland* (Scannell & Synnott 1987).

Scientific names follow for the most part *Flora Europaea* (Tutin *et al.* 1964-80, with the recently revised Volume 1, 1993), and thus Scannell & Synnott (1987), rather than *New Flora of the British Isles* (Stace 1991).

Flora Europaea is an internationally recognised and respected work that is a synthesis of current thinking on European plant classification. It has been followed by most European projects and has been adopted by the EU and Council of Europe as a standard text for the purpose of legal definition. There are some deviations from *Flora Europaea* in our text, based on recent research, such as in the dock and knotweed family; also intraspecific names do not always follow *Flora Europaea*, as the subspecies, varieties and other categories used will not always have been included in that work.

Subspecies and varieties are used to denote distinct variants of species that can be recognised by the field botanist. In general, a subspecies has a particular geographical or ecological range, for example restricted to Ireland or to parts of Ireland and Britain or to coastal habitats, whereas a variety has a more sporadic distribution. These categories draw attention to the richness and variation within the flora.

English names are based on, but do not follow rigidly, the Botanical Society of the British Isles' publication *English Names of Wildflowers* (Dony, Jury & Perring 1986), a standard list used by weed scientists and others.

Irish names follow Scannell & Synnott (1987), which provides a standard list of names in English and Irish. We have added a number of Irish names for introduced plants provided by An Buanchoiste Téarmaíochta (The Permanent Terminology Committee of the Department of Education) in Dublin.

Exclamation marks, initials (with date) and abbreviations accompany many plant records. All records made or confirmed over the period 1990-95 are denoted by an exclamation mark (!).

Where a plant is particularly rare or noteworthy, or there is no recent record, we have included the initials of the recorder(s). A full name followed by a date indicates a published literature reference.

Recorders' initials: JRA (John Akeroyd), KRB (Khaled Balabil), DB (Dave Bird), FAB (Frank Bisby), MB (Mary Bridges), JHB (John Burnett) TC (Terry Carruthers), KC (Karen Clarke), JC (Jacinta Crowley), JD (Jack Donovan), RF (Rosemary FitzGerald), PCH (Pat Hatch), PSWJ (Peter Wyse Jackson), SLJ (Stephen Jury), PK (Paul Kay), BJL (Bronwyn Leeder), HJL (H. Joan Lennon), BM (Beth Milner), TO'M (Tony O'Mahony), RAP (Robert Phillips), OP (Oleg Polunin), MQ (Michael Quirke), MWR (Mike Robinson), NR (Nick Rowe), JS (Jennifer Shockley), NS (Nick Stewart), DAW (David Webb), PW (Pat Whelan) and LCW (Lucy Wright).

References to herbarium specimens: BM (Natural History Museum, London), **CGE** (Botany School, University of Cambridge), **DBN** (National Botanic Gardens, Glasnevin, Dublin), **K** (Royal Botanic Gardens, Kew, London), **OXF** (Fielding-Druce Herbarium, University of Oxford), **TCD** (Trinity College, Dublin), **STH** (University of Southampton).

Symbols in the text

!   indicates that a plant has been confirmed during 1990-95 by botanists from Sherkin Island Marine Station.

*   indicates that a plant is not native and clearly introduced.

[ ]   indicates that a plant is extinct or presumed extinct.

PTERIDOPHYTES: ferns and fern allies (Nos 1 - 20)

Like much of Ireland, especially the west, Roaringwater Bay has a rich flora of ferns and fern-allies. These plants thrive in the moist, mild Atlantic climate of West Cork. They lack flowers and reproduce by dust-like spores instead of seeds.

EQUISETACEAE - horsetails

1. *Equisetum fluviatile* L.   **Water Horsetail, Scuab eich uisce**

Occasional in pools, marshes, wet meadows and ditches.

Sherkin!, Horse!

Rare in the islands but recorded from a number of places on the adjacent mainland. Records of Marsh Horsetail (*E. palustre* L.) from Sherkin may refer to this species; Great Horsetail (*E. telmateia* Ehrh.) has been reported from Cape Clear but needs to be confirmed.

2. *Equisetum arvense* L.   **Field Horsetail, Scuab eich ghoirt**

Locally frequent in moist, somewhat shaded places.

Sherkin!, Cape Clear!, Long!, Horse!, Heir!

OPHIOGLOSSACEAE - adder's tongue ferns

3. *Ophioglossum vulgatum* **L.**   **Adder's Tongue, Lus na teanga**

Rare in grassy heathland by the sea.

Sherkin (near Sherkin Point, KC 1992; near Trabawn, LCW 1982)!

Although this fern is scattered throughout Ireland, there are no other post-1950 records from Co. Cork (Jermy *et al.* 1978, p.28). It is an inconspicuous plant that should be sought elsewhere in short grassy swards near the sea. Small Adder's Tongue (*O. azoricum* Presl), recorded from several places in the Dingle Peninsula of Kerry, may also be present in similar habitats.

OSMUNDACEAE - royal ferns

4. *Osmunda regalis* **L.**   **Royal Fern, Raithneach ríúil**

Local in bogs, ditches, by streams and on earth cliffs near the sea.

Sherkin!, Cape Clear!, E Calf!, Long!, Castle!, Horse!, Skeam W!, Heir!, Spanish!

POLYPODIACEAE - polypody ferns

5. *Polypodium interjectum* **Shivas**   **Intermediate Polypody, Scim mheánach**

Abundant on walls and rocks.

Sherkin!, Cape Clear!, Calfs!, Goat!, Long!, Castle!, Horse!, Skeams!, Heir!, Catalogues!, Jeremy!, Spanish!, Inishleigh!, Mannin!

Some collections, from Sherkin and other islands, have been identified as Common Polypody (*Polypodium vulgare* L.). More study is needed.

HYPOLEPIDACEAE (DENNSTAEDTIACEAE) - bracken

6. *Pteridium aquilinum* **(L.) Kuhn**   **Bracken, Raithneach mhór**

Ubiquitous dominant fern of abandoned fields, hillsides and road-verges; spreading in the islands, having formerly been controlled by trampling and the browsing of young growth by stock. Cover provided by Bracken allows woodland plants to grow in the open.

Sherkin!, Cape Clear!, Calfs!, Goat!, Long!, Castle!, Horse!, Skeams!, Heir!, Catalogues!, Quarantine (LCW 1982), Jeremy!, Spanish!, Inishleigh!, Mannin!

ASPLENIACEAE - spleenwort ferns

7. *Asplenium scolopendrium* **L.** (*Phyllitis scolopendrium* **(L.) Newman**)

Hart's-tongue Fern, Creamh na muice fia

Shady banks, ditches and bases of walls.

Sherkin!, Cape Clear!, E Calf!, Goat!, Long!, Horse!, Skeam E!, Heir!, Spanish!

Often a somewhat lime-loving species.

8. *Asplenium adiantum-nigrum* **L.**   **Black Spleenwort, Fionncha dubh**

Common in crevices of walls and rocks.

Sherkin!, Cape Clear!, Calfs!, Goat!, Long!, Castle!, Horse!, Skeams!, Heir!, Sandy!, Spanish!, Mannin!

9. *Asplenium obovatum* **Viv. subsp.** *lanceolatum* **(Fiori) Pinto da Silva (*A. billotii* F. Schultz)**

Lanceolate Spleenwort, Fionncha lansach

Rare and in small numbers in damp, shady places in crevices of stonework and unmortared walls and earth cliffs near the sea. **Irish Red Data Book - Vulnerable.**

Sherkin (Horseshoe Harbour area, PCH & MWR 1994)!, Cape Clear (South Harbour, confirming records of RAP 1896-1902, JD 1992; North Harbour, PCH & MWR 1994)!, Long (JRA, PCH & MWR 1994)!, Castle (PCH & MWR 1994)!

Reported in the late 19th Century from several stations in Co. Cork, including Phillips' 1896 record from near South Harbour (Colgan & Scully 1898), but not seen again until 1992 (several JD records held at Bird Observatory). A rare plant in Ireland, it is also known from Co. Wexford, and elsewhere in West Cork (for example, seen at Baltimore, PCH & MWR 1994) and Kerry (P. Wyse Jackson, pers. comm.).

Subsp. *lanceolatum* occurs in western Europe, extending eastwards to Switzerland and southwards to southern Italy; subsp. *obovatum* has a mostly Mediterranean distribution.

10. *Asplenium ruta-muraria* **L.**   **Wall Spleenwort, Luibh na seacht ngábh**

Rare in crevices of mortared walls.

Heir (walls outside old school house, JRA & NR 1993)!, Cape Clear (Edmunds 1960).

11. *Asplenium marinum* **L.**   **Sea Spleenwort, Fionncha mara**

Crevices of rocks and walls by the sea, in sites exposed to salt spray.

Sherkin!, Cape Clear!, Calfs!, Goat!, Long!, Castle!, Horse!, Skeam W!, Heir!, Catalogues!, Sandy!, Spanish!, Mannin (PW 1975).

12. *Asplenium trichomanes* **L.**   **Maidenhair Spleenwort, Lus na seilge**

Common in crevices of walls.

Sherkin!, Cape Clear!, W & M Calf!, Goat!, Long!, Castle!, Horse!, Skeam E!, Heir!, Spanish!, Mannin!

Three subspecies are recorded from the British Isles, but the Roaringwater Bay plants are all subsp. *trichomanes*, the commoner variant on acid rocks.

13. *Asplenium ceterach* **L. (*Ceterach officinarum* DC.)**

Rustyback Fern, Raithneach rua

Rare in crevices of mortared walls.

Sherkin (sparingly on roadside wall by Cow Strand, JRA & NR 1993; house at Farranacoush, PCH & MWR 1995)!, Heir (walls outside old school house)!

A lime-loving plant limited by the acid nature of most habitats. Not recorded in the islands by Jermy *et al.* (1978, p.66). This fern also occurs on the pier at Schull.

WOODSIACEAE (ATHYRIACEAE) - lady ferns

14. *Athyrium filix-femina* **(L.) Roth**　　　　　　**Lady-fern, Raithneach Mhuire**

Locally common in roadside ditches, by streams and at base of walls.

Sherkin!, Cape Clear!, W Calf!, Long!, Castle!, Horse!, Skeam E!, Heir!, Spanish!, Mannin!

DRYOPTERIDACEAE - shield, male and buckler ferns

15. *Polystichum setiferum* **(Forskal) Woynar**　　　**Soft Shield-fern, Ibheag bhog**

Occasional on sheltered banks and by walls on larger islands.

Sherkin!, Long (PW 1975), Horse!, Skeam E!, Heir!, Spanish!

A local plant in West Cork and Kerry (see Jermy *et al.* 1978, p.80).

16. *Dryopteris filix-mas* **(L.) Schott**　　　　　**Male-fern, Raithneach mhadra**

Shady roadsides, and the base of walls and banks on larger islands.

Sherkin!, Cape Clear!, Long!, Castle!, Horse!, Skeam E!, Heir!, Spanish!, Mannin!

The commonest male or buckler-fern species in the Roaringwater Bay area.

17. *Dryopteris affinis* **(Lowe) Frazer-Jenkins subsp.** *borreri* **(***D. borreri* **(Newman) Newman ex Oberholzer & Tavel)**

　　　　　　　　　　　　　　　　　　Scaly Male-fern, Raithneach ghainneach

Shady roadsides and base of walls and banks on larger islands.

Sherkin!, Cape Clear!, Long!, Castle!, Horse!, Heir!

18. *Dryopteris aemula* **(Aiton) O. Kuntze**

　　　　　　　　　　　　　　　Hay-scented Buckler-fern, Raithneach chumhra

Rare on sheltered banks and walls of lanes.

Sherkin (road to The Dock)!, Cape Clear (near turbot farm)!, Long (W. end)!, Castle!

The Irish populations of this rare European fern are of international importance. The yellowish-green, slightly crisped fronds are distinctive.

19. *Dryopteris dilatata* **(Hoffm.) A. Gray (***D. austriaca* **auct.)**

　　　　　　　　　　　　　　　　　Broad Buckler-fern, Raithneach leathan

Local on roadside banks, at base of walls and in ditches, mostly on the larger islands.

Sherkin!, Cape Clear!, W Calf!, Long!, Castle!, Horse!, Skeam W!, Heir!, Mannin!

BLECHNACEAE - hard ferns

20. *Blechnum spicant* **(L.) Roth**　　　　　　　　**Hard Fern, Raithneach chrua**

Local on heathy banks, where the soil is well-drained.

Sherkin!, Cape Clear!, E Calf (JC 1975), Goat!, Long!, Castle!, Horse!, Heir!, Spanish!, Mannin!

GYMNOSPERMS: Conifers (Nos 21 - 25)

Ireland has only three native conifers, Scots Pine (*Pinus sylvestris* L., believed to be long extinct as a native plant), Yew (*Taxus baccata* L.) and Juniper (*Juniperus communis* L.). None occur in Roaringwater Bay, but exotic conifers have been planted here and there for shelter and ornament. These woody plants have cones or fleshy, berry-like structures rather than flowers.

PINACEAE - pines, spruces and firs

*21. *Picea sitchensis* **(Bong.) Carriere** **Sitka Spruce, Sprús Sitceach**

Planted in shelter belts.

Sherkin!, Cape Clear!, Skeam E!, Heir!

A native of western North America that is widely planted on wetter soils in Ireland and elsewhere in north-western Europe.

*22. *Pinus nigra* **Arnold subsp.** *nigra* **Austrian Pine, Péine Ostarach**

Planted in shelter belts and gardens.

Sherkin!, Cape Clear!, Skeam E!, Heir!

A native of the mountains of Europe. Unconfirmed records of Maritime Pine (*P. pinaster*) and Scots Pine (*P. sylvestris*) probably belong here.

*23. *Pinus radiata* **D. Don** **Monterey Pine, Péine Monterey**

Planted in shelter belts and around gardens.

Sherkin!, Cape Clear!, Heir!

Like the next species, originally from the coasts and islands of southern California, this 3-needled pine (Austrian Pine has 2-needled shoots) is widely planted for shelter near coasts in Ireland and Britain. It withstands salt-laden winds better than most other trees.

CUPRESSACEAE - cypresses

*24. *Cupressus macrocarpa* **Hartweg ex Gordon** **Monterey Cypress, Cufróg Monterey**

Occasionally planted for shelter and ornament.

Sherkin (Kinish Harbour; by church)!, Skeam E (LCW 1982).

*25. *X Cupressocyparis leylandii* **(A.G. Jackson & Dallimore) Dallimore**

Leyland Cypress, Cufróg Leyland

Occasionally planted in shelter belts. A hybrid of garden origin.

Sherkin (W. end, for example near harbour)!

ANGIOSPERMS: Flowering Plants (Nos. 26 - 590)

SALICACEAE – poplars, sallies and willows

Small trees or shrubs of damp or wet ground, willows are widely planted for shelter, ornament and their flexible twigs, used in basket-making. They are important hedgerow plants in large areas of West Cork.

*26. *Salix fragilis* **L. var.** *fragilis*   **Crack Willow, Saileach bhriosc**

Planted in hedges.

Sherkin!, Long!, Castle (Allin 1883), Horse!, Heir!

*27. *Salix alba L. x fragilis* **(*S. x rubens* Schrank)**

Planted near buildings.

Castle (PCH & MWR 1994)!, Heir (Polunin 1950).

A specimen from Castle was confirmed by R.D. Meikle (who had identified the willows collected by Polunin). He noted that the leaves of the specimen had a thin indumentum [covering of hairs] and well-developed teeth on the margins. This hybrid is variable.

A rare plant in Co. Cork; Polunin (1950) made the first Co. Cork record since Power (1845) had reported this hybrid from Carragaline, near Cork City.

28. *Salix atrocinerea* **Brot. (*S. cinerea* L. subsp.** *oleifolia* **Macreight)**

       Rusty Willow, Saileach rua

Hedges, scrub; a wind-tolerant species.

Sherkin!, Cape Clear!, M Calf!, Long!, Castle!, Horse!, Skeam W!, Heir!, Catalogues!, Spanish!

A record from Horse of Grey Willow (*S. cinerea* L.), a much rarer plant of Central and Northern Ireland, probably belongs here. Irish and British botanists usually treat Rusty and Grey Willow as subspecies.

29. *Salix aurita* **L.**   **Eared Willow, Crann sníofa**

Widespread: the commonest larger willow on the islands.

Sherkin!, Cape Clear!, Long!, Castle!, Horse!, Skeam W!, Heir!, Catalogues!, Sandy (LCW 1982), Spanish!, Inishleigh!, Mannin!

30. *Salix aurita x atrocinearea* **(*S. x multinervis* Doell)**

Occasional in hedges.

Horse (NR 1993)!, Heir (JRA & NR 1993)!

*31. *Salix x calodendron* **Wimm. (*S. aurita x cinerea x viminalis*)**

       Jargomel Sallow, Saileach Jargomel

Heir (Polunin 1950).

A triple hybrid willow, introduced to Ireland, mostly in Ulster; perhaps originally from Holland. It almost certainly survives on Heir.

*32. *Salix caprea* L.   **Goat Willow, Sailchearnach**

Hedges, usually near houses or ruins; probably introduced.

Sherkin (near Cow Strand)!, Horse!, Heir (near East Pier)!, Spanish!

*33. *Salix* x *sericans* Tausch ex A. Kerner (*S. caprea x viminalis*)

Planted near houses.

Castle (PCH & MWR 1994)!, Heir (BM 1995)!

A widespread hybrid in Ireland but not previously reported from West Cork.

34. *Salix repens* L. subsp. *repens*   **Creeping Willow, Saileach reatha**

Widespread on heaths, banks and rocky ground.

Sherkin!, Cape Clear!, Calfs!, Goat!, Long!, Castle!, Horse!, Skeam W!, Heir!, Catalogues!, Sandy!, Spanish!, Inishleigh!, Mannin!

*35. *Salix viminalis* L.   **Almond Willow or Osier, Saileánach**

Sherkin!, Cape Clear!, Castle!, Horse!, Heir!

Probably introduced; the willow of the basket-maker. Baskets are still made in the islands.

*36. *Populus tremula* L.   **Aspen, Crann creathach**

Occasionally planted for shelter or ornament.

Long!, Horse (recently planted, 1994)!

*37. *Populus x canadensis* Moench var. *serotina* (Hartig) Rehder

                                                      Italian Poplar, Poibleog ghallda

Planted here and there for shelter and ornament; suckering to form patches.

Sherkin!, Cape Clear (probably the poplar recorded by Edmunds 1960 and TC 1985)!, Long!, Heir!

BETULACEAE - birches, alders and hazels

Downy Birch (*Betula pubescens*) has been planted recently on Horse for ornament and shelter. Birch pollen is recorded from mud deposits in Lough Ordree on Sherkin, but this tree has probably been extinct in the islands for centuries.

38. *Alnus glutinosa* (L.) Gaertner   **Alder, Fearnóg**

Sheltered places, mostly by streams.

Sherkin!, Cape Clear (South Harbour, planted)!, Long!, Heir (E. end, probably planted)!

39. *Corylus avellana* L. Hazel, Coll

In scrub or forming small stands with other woody plants.

Sherkin (near Castle)!, Horse (E. end)!, Spanish!

Perhaps introduced, but formerly a widespread woodland tree in West Cork. On Horse it occurs with Spindle in a gully on a low sea-cliff, which suggests a native population.

FAGACEAE - oaks, chestnuts and beeches

*40. *Castanea sativa* Miller Sweet Chestnut, Castán

Cape Clear (recently planted)!, Spanish (one tree only)!

Planted; introduced to Ireland from Britain, to where it had been brought from the Mediterranean region by the Romans.

41. *Quercus petraea* (Mattuschka) Liebl. Sessile Oak, Dair ghaelach

Occasional in hedges and as individual small trees.

Sherkin (School, OP, unpublished notes; near Church; also planted just south of Lough Ordree)!, Cape Clear (probably the oak recorded by Sharrock 1965 and TC 1985), Spanish!, Mannin (NR 1993)!

The commoner of the two native oaks. It grows on wetter soils in Ireland and once formed extensive woodlands in West Cork.

ULMACEAE - elms

*42. *Ulmus procera* Salisb. English Elm, Leamhán gallda

Widespread on some islands, locally forming small, shady copses.

Sherkin (mostly towards E. end and around houses)!, Cape Clear (South Harbour)!, Horse (around settlement at E. end)!, Spanish (LCW 1982).

Planted for shelter and suckering in places, especially around Kinish Harbour on Sherkin. Widely introduced in Ireland and only doubtfully native even in Britain. Wych Elm (*U. glabra* Hudson) has been reported from Sherkin in error for this species.

CANNABACEAE - hops and hemp

*43. *Humulus lupulus* L. Hop, Hopa

Rare in thickets near houses.

Sherkin (lane to Marine Station near The Cross; cliffs close to Abbey, Polunin 1949)!

Also reported from Schull (RAP 1894). Introduced in Ireland, presumably as elsewhere for flavouring and preserving beer, although perhaps native in southern England in wet woods.

URTICACEAE - nettles

44. *Urtica dioica* **L.**   **Stinging Nettle, Neantóg**

Abundant in fields, road-verges and waste places, especially around deserted houses and farms.

Sherkin!, Cape Clear!, Calfs!, Carthys!, Long!, Castle!, Horse!, Skeams!, Heir!, Catalogues!, Sandy!, Spanish!, Inishleigh (LCW 1982), Mannin!

45. *Urtica urens* **L.**   **Small Nettle, Neantóg bheag**

Rare around ruined buildings, and on disturbed ground and strands.

Sherkin (Polunin 1949), Cape Clear (Edmonds 1960 and more recent records held at Bird Observatory), Castle (BM & MWR 1995)!, Skeam E!

*46. *Soleirolea soleirolii* **(Req.) Dandy**   **Mother-of-thousands, Lus na ndeor**

Gardens, escaping and becoming naturalised on shady banks and at bases of walls.

Sherkin!

Locally frequent at Baltimore, by the harbour and the road to the south of the town. Native to the islands of the western Mediterranean.

*47. *Parietaria judaica* **L.**   **Pellitory-of-the-wall, Feabhraíd**

Local on walls, both in crevices and at the base.

Sherkin!, Cape Clear!, Castle!, Skeam E!, Spanish!

Commonest on Sherkin around the Castle, Abbey and church, but here and there elsewhere; abundant on ruined houses on Skeam East. It also grows on the Castle at Baltimore. Probably it survives as a relic of its former use as a medicinal plant, as elsewhere in Ireland (Synnott 1979) and in Britain (Howes 1993).

POLYGONACEAE – docks and knotgrasses

Most members of this family in West Cork, and Ireland generally, are weeds of cultivated land or plants of disturbed ground and strands.

48. *Polygonum oxyspermum* **C.A. Meyer & Bunge ex Ledeb. subsp.** *raii* **(Bab.) D.A. Webb & Chater**

                                    Ray's Knotgrass, Glúineach ghlé

Occasional and rather sporadic on sand or shingle strands.

Sherkin (Tragowenmore [Cow Strand], Polunin 1949; Trabawn; The Dock; path at Marine Station, introduced with beach sand, JRA 1994)!, E Calf!, Long (W. end)!

A local plant in Ireland and distinctly rare in the west.

49. *Polygonum aviculare* **L.**   **Common Knotgrass, Glúineach bheag**

Common on waysides, waste ground and cultivated land; sometimes on bird islands.

Sherkin!, Cape Clear!, Badger!, Calfs!, Carthys!, Long!, Castle!, Horse!, Skeams!, Heir!, Catalogues!, Sandy!, Spanish!, Inishleigh!, Mannin!

50. *Polygonum arenastrum* **Boreau**   **Equal-leaved Knotgrass, Glúineach ghainimh**

Locally common on tracks and trampled ground.

Sherkin!, Cape Clear!, W & M Calf!, Skeam E!, Heir!, Spanish (LCW 1982).

This species is too little recorded in Ireland, as elsewhere in Europe. Similar to Common Knotgrass, it can be distinguished by the leaves that are more or less equal in size and often blunt, and the perianth-tube about the same length as the free segments. It is almost always prostrate, forming a compact mat.

51. *Persicaria hydropiper* **(L.) Spach (***Polygonum hydropiper* **L.)**

Water-pepper, Biorphiobar

Occasional in marshy places, damp fields and roadsides.

Sherkin!, Cape Clear!, Calfs!, Long!, Castle!, Horse!, Heir!, Spanish!

Easily distinguished from the other *Persicaria* species by the peppery taste, the large, cleistogamous flower in each leaf-angle and the flat, brown glands that dot the perianth.

52. *Persicaria maculosa* **Gray (***Polygonum persicaria* **L.)**

Persicaria, Glúineach dhearg

Cultivated ground and poorly drained pastures; occasionally on waysides and bird islands.

Sherkin!, Cape Clear!, Badger!, Calfs!, Long!, Castle!, Horse!, Skeam E!, Heir!, Spanish!, Inishleigh!

Records from Sherkin of Tasteless Water-pepper (*P. laxiflora* (Weihe) Opiz), a very rare Irish plant, perhaps native only around Lough Neagh in Ulster, belong to this species. The bright pink flowers of Persicaria are distinctive in the field.

53. *Persicaria lapathifolia* **(L.) Gray (***Polygonum lapathifolium* **L.,** *P. nodosum* **Pers.)**

Pale Persicaria, Glúineach bhán

Rather rare on cultivated ground.

Sherkin!, Long!, Castle!, Heir!, Spanish!

Probably under-recorded; distinguished from Persicaria by the yellow, stalkless glands that give a rough feel to the stalks of the flower-heads, and the dull pink flowers.

54. *Persicaria amphibia* **(L.) Gray (***Polygonum amphibium* **L.)**

Amphibious Bistort, Glúineach uisce

Locally common in loughs and ditches; forming a pink band in summer on the southern shore of Lough Errul on Cape Clear.

Sherkin (Lough Ordree, Trabawn)!, Cape Clear (especially Lough Errul)!, E Calf!, Long!, Heir!

55. *Fallopia convolvulus* **(L.) A. Löve (***Polygonum convolvulus* **L.)**

Black Bindweed, Glúineach dhubh

Occasional on cultivated or disturbed ground. It was very abundant in 1995.

Sherkin!, Cape Clear!, Long!, Horse!, Skeam E!, Heir!

Formerly a major contaminent of agricultural seed in Ireland and elsewhere.

*56. *Fallopia japonica* (**Houtt.**) **Ronce Decraene** (*Polygonum cuspidatum* **Siebold & Zucc.**)

Japanese Knotweed, Glúineach bhiorach

Occasional, locally forming thickets.

Sherkin!, Cape Clear (South Harbour and elsewhere)!, Long!

This invasive plant also occurs near to the pier on Turk Head.

57. *Rumex acetosella* L. **Sheep's Sorrel, Samhadh caorach**

Common on heathland, in rocky fields and on wall-tops.

Sherkin!, Cape Clear!, Calfs!, Long!, Castle!, Horse!, Skeams!, Heir!, Catalogues!, Sandy!, Quarantine!, Jeremy!, Spanish!, Inishleigh!, Mannin!

All the fruiting plants examined belong to subsp. *pyrenaicus* (Pourret ex Lapeyr.) Akeroyd (*R. angiocarpus* Murb.), which has a single pair of basal leaf-lobes and perianth-segments attached firmly to the ripe fruits. This is the widespread plant in Ireland and most of western and southern Britain; also over most of W. and S.W. Europe.

58. *Rumex acetosa* L. **Common Sorrel, Samhadh bó**

Common in grassland and on road verges, waste places, shingle strands and cliffs.

Sherkin!, Cape Clear!, Badger!, Calfs!, Carthys!, Goat!, Little Goat!, Long!, Castle!, Horse!, Skeams!, Heir!, Catalogues!, Sandy!, Quarantine!, Jeremy!, Spanish!, Inishleigh!, Mannin!

Robust plants from cliffs and bird islands, with dark green, fleshy leaves and rather dense clusters of flowers, approach subsp. *biformis* (Lange) Castroviejo & Valdés-Bermejo, described from the coasts of north-west Spain but present as far north as the west of Scotland.

59. *Rumex crispus* L. **Curled Dock, Copóg chatach**

Common on waysides, disturbed and cultivated ground; strands, blown sand, rocks on the upper shore and sea-cliffs.

Sherkin!, Cape Clear!, Badger!, Calfs!, Carthys!, Goat!, Little Goat!, Long!, Castle!, Horse!, Skeams!, Heir!, Catalogues!, Sandy!, Quarantine!, Jeremy!, Spanish!, Inishleigh!, Mannin!

Many plants belong to subsp. *littoreus* (Hardy) Akeroyd, characterised by dense clusters of flowers, large fruits and well-developed corky tubercles on the perianth-segments, a variant of beaches and coastal rocks and cliffs. However, a good proportion of plants from Sherkin at least are intermediate between this and subsp. *crispus*, the weed of cultivated ground.

60. *Rumex x pratensis* **Mert. & Koch** (*R. crispus x obtusifolius*)

Waysides, waste ground and pastures.

Sherkin!, Long!, Horse!, Heir!

This robust plant, the commonest hybrid dock in Ireland and Britain, can be recognised by the tall habit, reddish, irregularly toothed fruits, many of which fall early, and vigorous regrowth from the base in late summer and autumn.

A record of Water Dock (*R. hydrolapathum* Hudson) from Sherkin probably belongs here; this large aquatic dock is commonest in the Midlands, although it does have a few stations in the west, including the Dingle peninsula in Kerry.

61. *Rumex conglomeratus* **Murray**   **Clustered Dock, Copóg thriopallach**

Locally abundant in damp fields and on disturbed waysides.

Sherkin!, Cape Clear!, Calfs!, Carthys!, Long!, Castle!, Horse!, Skeams!, Heir!, Sandy!, Quarantine!, Spanish!, Inishleigh!, Mannin!

62. *Rumex sanguineus* **L. var.** *viridis* **Sibth.**   **Wood Dock, Copóg choille**

Local in shady lanes and hedge-banks.

Sherkin (mostly along main road)!, Heir!, Spanish!

The single, almost globular, corky tubercle on the fruits distinguishes this plant from the similar Clustered Dock, which has 3-tubercled fruits.

63. *Rumex x ruhmeri* **Hausskn. (***R. conglomeratus x sanguineus***)**

Shady roadsides and disturbed pastures.

Sherkin (from S. of Trabawn to Island House, JRA 1993-4)!

Previously reported from Ireland only from near Duleek, Co. Meath (Kelly & Doogue 1990), although widespread in parts of Britain, where the two species apparently cross and backcross.

64. *Rumex x muretii* **Hausskn. (***R. conglomeratus x pulcher***)**

Pastures near the sea.

Sherkin (Horseshoe Harbour, JRA & NR 1993; S. of Trabawn, JRA 1994)!

Not previously reported from Ireland, although known from several places in southern England. Hybrids between Fiddle Dock and Curled and Broad-leaved Dock should be looked for on Sherkin.

65. *Rumex pulcher* **L.**   **Fiddle Dock, Copóg chumtha**

Rare in grassland near houses and tracks.

Sherkin (between Post Office and Horseshoe Harbour; one plant in patch of hybrids with Clustered Dock, S. of Trabawn, JRA 1994)!, Cape Clear (RAP 1896-1902; *O. Polunin 201*, 8.1948, **BM**), Heir (RAP 1896-1902).

Ten plants of this scarce Irish dock were located in 1992, in two small colonies between the Abbey and Horseshoe Harbour, confirming reports from the area by Polunin (1950) and earlier workers. Since the species has persisted for nearly 100 years on Sherkin, has been repeatedly recorded in Co. Wexford and is a member of native plant communities (Akeroyd 1993), it cannot be regarded as merely "casual" (Perring & Walters 1976) and has a strong claim to be a native of Ireland. The zig-zag branches and fiddle-shaped basal leaves are distinctive.

In 1993 there were over 100 plants in pastures at Horseshoe Harbour, but this rare plant should be monitored carefully. Phillips also noted Fiddle Dock from Baltimore (RAP 1896-1902; "plentiful" there, Colgan & Scully 1898), but it has not been recorded there since.

66. *Rumex obtusifolius* **L.**   **Broad-leaved Dock, Copóg shráide**

Waysides and cultivated ground; the commonest dock and often a pestilential weed.

Sherkin!, Cape Clear!, Calfs!, Carthys!, Goat!, Long!, Castle!, Horse!, Skeams!, Heir!, Catalogues!, Spanish!, Inishleigh!

CHENOPODIACEAE – beets, goosefoots and oraches

These are plants of seashores or disturbed, manure-rich ground. The seeds or leaves of several species have long been used for food. The flowers are green and inconspicuous.

67. *Beta vulgaris* **L. subsp.** *maritima* **(L.) Arcangeli** Sea Beet, Laíon na trá

Frequent on sea-cliffs, rocks and strands; perennial.

Sherkin!, Cape Clear!, Bird!, Badger!, Calfs!, Carthys!, Goat!, Long!, Castle!, Horse!, Skeam W!, Heir!, Jeremy!, Inishleigh!

*68. *Beta vulgaris* **L. subsp.** *vulgaris* Fodder Beet, Biatas beithíoch

Grown in small quantity on Sherkin and probably elsewhere to feed cattle, sometimes persisting as a weed; biennial.

Sherkin!, Skeam W (JRA & NR 1993)!

Fodder Beet is similar in general appearance to Sugar Beet. Other beets, such as Beetroot and Spinach Beet, are grown in gardens.

*69. *Chenopodium bonus-henricus* **L.** Good King Henry, Praiseach bhráthar

Amongst nettles by ruined buildings.

Castle (PCH & MWR 1994)!

Allin (1883) reported this rare Irish plant, usually associated with old buildings, from Durrus on the mainland. Native to the mountains of central & southern Europe, it has long been introduced further afield as a vegetable similar to spinach.

70. *Chenopodium rubrum* **L.** Red Goosefoot, Blonagán dearg

Rare in and around dried-up boggy pools near sea.

Sherkin (BM 1995, confirming record of Polunin 1950)!, W Calf (confirming record of Polunin 1950)!, M Calf (BM 1995)!, E Calf (NR 1993, PCH & MWR 1994)!, Carthys (LCW 1982).

On the basis of Polunin specimens (**BM**) examined by JRA, at least some plants from Sherkin and West Calf belong to the dwarf var. *pseudobotryoides* Syme. The plants found in 1994-5 were mostly robust and erect.

During the hot, dry summer of 1995, with the reduced water levels in brackish pools, this species was especially abundant. Polunin's records were originally made in 1947 during another notably dry summer.

71. *Chenopodium album* **L.** Fat Hen, Blonagán bán

Sometimes common on cultivated ground and a bad weed of potatoes.

Sherkin!, Cape Clear!, Carthys!, Castle!, Skeam E!, Heir!

The leaves of this plant were long used as a substitute for spinach and the seeds were gathered as a starch-rich grain.

72.   *Atriplex laciniata* L.   **Frosted Orache, Eilifleog phlúrach**

Local on sandy strands.

Sherkin!, E Calf!, Long!, Heir!

The record of Polunin (1950) was the first from western Ireland. It is now know from several stations in Connemara and elsewhere (Webb & Scannell 1983); O'Mahony (1975) cites records from Mid & East Cork. The 'frosted' appearance of the leaves is distinctive.

73.   *Atriplex patula* L.   **Common Orache, Eilifleog chaol**

Common on cultivated land.

Sherkin!, Cape Clear!, Badger!, Calfs!, Little Goat (NR 1993)!, Long!, Castle!, Horse!, Skeams!, Heir!, Catalogues!, Spanish!

74.   *Atriplex prostrata* **Boucher ex DC.** (*A. hastata* **auct.**)

Spear-leaved Orache, Eilifleog leathan

Often abundant on strands, the upper levels of saltmarshes and waste ground by the sea.

Sherkin!, Cape Clear!, Bird!, Badger!, Calfs!, Carthys! Long!, Horse!, Skeams!, Heir!, Spanish!, Inishleigh!

75.   *Atriplex glabriuscula* **Edmonston**   **Babington's Orache, Eilifleog chladaigh**

Common on sand and shingle strands.

Sherkin!, Cape Clear!, W Calf (LCW 1982), M & E Calf!, Carthys!, Long!, Castle (LCW 1982), Horse!, Skeams!, Heir!, Catalogues!, Sandy!, Quarantine!, Jeremy!, Spanish!, Inishleigh!, Mannin!

The typical plant of exposed shingle strands; a more prostrate plant than Spear-leaved Orache, with tapered rather than cut-off leaf-bases and fruiting bracts fused to halfway. Some plants are undoubtedly hybrids between this species and Spear-leaved Orache, as reported by Polunin (1950), who also reported the hybrid with Common Orache. These need more study.

76.   *Salicornia europaea* L.   **Glasswort, Lus na gloine**

Locally common in saltmarshes.

Sherkin (Kinish Harbour, The Dock)!, Long!, Heir!, Sandy!, Quarantine!, Spanish!, Inishleigh!

A record of the closely related *S. ramosissima* J.Woods from Illaunroemor, north of Mannin, requires confirmation. Glassworts need further study in Ireland.

77.   *Suaeda maritima* **(L.) Dumort.**   **Annual Sea-blite, Blide mhara**

Frequent in saltmarshes and on muddy shingle strands.

Sherkin!, E Calf (JS 1990)!, Heir!, Quarantine!, Spanish!, Inishleigh!

78.   *Salsola kali* L.   **Prickly Saltwort, Lus an tsalainn**

Rare and sporadic on sandy strands.

Sherkin (JS 1990, confirming record of Polunin 1949)!

PORTULACACEAE - blinks

79. *Montia fontana* **L.**   **Blinks, Fliodh uisce**

Wet, muddy ground and ditches.

Sherkin!, Cape Clear!, M Calf!, Castle!, Horse!, Heir!, Spanish!

The plants on Horse, growing in damp, short coastal grassland, with an erect habit and papillose seeds, belong to subsp. *chondrosperma* (Fenzl) Walters. This variant is rare in Ireland, until recently known only from the Beara peninsula (Perring & Sell 1968), but now becoming a weed in Co. Kildare on cutover bog being reclaimed for tillage or forestry (Curran 1985).

CARYOPHYLLACEAE – campions, chickweeds, pearlworts and spurreys

Many members of this family grow in open ground and on seashores. Others, such as Pinks and Carnations, are popular garden plants.

80. *Arenaria serpyllifolia* **L. subsp.** *serpyllifolia*

Thyme-leaved Sandwort, Gaineamhlus tíme

Open, sandy ground near the sea.

Sherkin!, Cape Clear!, E Calf!, Long!, Heir!

81. *Honkenya peploides* **(L.) Ehrh.**   **Sea Sandwort, Gaineamhlus mara**

Local but sometimes abundant on sand and fine shingle strands.

Sherkin!, M & E Calf!, Long!, Horse!, Heir!

82. *Stellaria media* **(L.) Vill.**   **Common Chickweed, Fliodh**

Abundant on cultivated and disturbed ground; also in dropping-enriched sites on bird islands and around rabbit burrows.

Sherkin!, Cape Clear!, Badger!, Calfs!, Carthys!, Little Goat!, Long!, Castle!, Horse!, Skeam E!, Heir!, Catalogues!, Spanish!, Mannin!

83. *Stellaria holostea* **L.**   **Greater Stitchwort, Tursarraing mhór**

Locally common on road-verges, heathy banks and fields.

Sherkin!, Castle (LCW 1982), Horse!, Spanish!, Mannin!

84. *Stellaria alsine* **Grimm**   **Bog Stichwort, Tursarraing mhóna**

Wet fields and marshes.

Sherkin!, Cape Clear!, E Calf!, Long!, Castle!, Horse!, Skeam E!, Heir!, Spanish!

Records of Marsh Stitchwort (*S. palustris* Retz.), a plant more characteristic of fens in the Midlands, probably belong here.

85. *Stellaria graminea* **L.**   **Lesser Stitchwort, Tursarraing bheag**

Dry heaths and banks.

Sherkin!, Cape Clear!, W & E Calf!, Long!, Castle!, Horse!, Skeam W!, Heir!, Catalogues!, Sandy!, Spanish!, Inishleigh!, Mannin!

86. *Cerastium fontanum* **Baumg. subsp.** *vulgare* **(Hartman) Greuter & Burdet (***C.*** *fontanum* **subsp.** *triviale* **(Murb.) Jalas)**

Common Mouse-ear Chickweed, Cluas luchóige

Grassland, waysides and cultivated ground.

Sherkin!, Cape Clear!, Calfs!, Carthys!, Goat!, Long!, Castle!, Horse!, Skeams!, Heir!, Catalogues!, Sandy!, Quarantine!, Jeremy!, Spanish!, Inishleigh!, Mannin!

87. *Cerastium fontanum* **Baumg. subsp.** *holosteoides* **(Fries) Salman** *et al.* **(***C.*** *holosteoides* **Fries)**

Wetter places than the other subspecies, often near the sea.

Sherkin!, Cape Clear!, Calfs!, Carthys!, Goat!, Long!, Castle!, Horse, Skeam W!, Heir!, Catalogues!, Sandy!, Jeremy!, Inishleigh!, Mannin!

88. *Cerastium glomeratum* **Thuill.**

Sticky Mouse-ear Chickweed, Cluas luchóige ghreamaitheach

Occasional on bare or cultivated ground.

Sherkin!, Cape Clear!, E Calf!, Carthys (LCW 1982), Long!, Castle!, Horse (*O. Polunin*, 8.1948, **BM**), Skeam E!, Heir!, Catalogues!

89. *Cerastium diffusum* **Pers. (***C.*** *atrovirens* **Bab.,** *C. tetrandrum* **Curtis)**

Sea Mouse-ear Chickweed, Cluas luchóige mhara

Local on sand-dunes and sandy ground by sea; sometimes on coastal cliffs and rocks.

Sherkin!, Cape Clear!, Calfs!, Little Goat!, Long!, Castle!, Horse!, Skeams!, Heir!, Catalogues!, Quarantine!, Spanish!

90. *Sagina nodosa* **(L.) Fenzl**   Knotted Pearlwort, Mongán glúineach

Short coastal grassland and heathland.

Sherkin (Trabawn)!, Cape Clear!, W & E Calf!, Long!, Horse!, Skeams!, Heir!, Spanish!

91. *Sagina subulata* **(Swartz) C. Presl**   Heath Pearlwort, Mongán móna

Short grassy swards and rocky ground in coastal heathland.

Sherkin (Horseshoe Harbour, Trabawn)!, Cape Clear (South Harbour)!, Long (W. end)!, Skeam E!, Heir!

A scarce plant in Ireland, mainly on western coasts.

92. *Sagina procumbens* **L.**   Procumbent Pearlwort, Mongán sínte

Common in dry and wet grassland, and on tracks and rocks.

Sherkin!, Cape Clear!, Bird!, Badger (LCW 1982), Calfs!, Carthys!, Goat!, Little Goat!, Long!, Castle!, Horse!, Skeams!, Heir!, Catalogues!, Sandy!, Spanish!, Inishleigh!, Mannin!

93. *Sagina apetala* **Ard. subsp.** *erecta*   **Annual Pearlwort, Mongán lom**

Widespread but inconspicuous in bare, rocky ground.

Sherkin!, Cape Clear!, W & M Calf!, Long!, Castle!, Horse!, Skeams!, Heir!, Sandy!, Quarantine (LCW 1982), Spanish!, Inishleigh (LCW 1982), Mannin!

94. *Sagina maritima* **G. Don fil.**   **Sea Pearlwort, Mongán mara**

Bare ground and rocks by the sea; tiny and often overlooked.

Sherkin!, Cape Clear!, W Calf!, Carthys!, Long!, Castle!, Skeams!, Heir!, Catalogues!, Jeremy!, Inishleigh!

95. *Spergula arvensis* **L.**   **Corn Spurrey, Corrán lín**

Cultivated and disturbed ground, sometimes locally common.

Sherkin!, Cape Clear!, Horse!, Heir!

96. *Spergularia rupicola* **Lebel ex Le Jolis**   **Rock Sea-spurrey, Cabróis na gcloch**

Common on coastal rocks and walls, including quays and castles.

Sherkin!, Cape Clear!, Bird!, Badger!, Calfs!, Carthys!, Goat!, Little Goat!, Long!, Castle!, Horse!, Skeams!, Heir!, Catalogues!, Sandy!, Quarantine!, Jeremy (LCW 1982), Spanish!, Inishleigh!, Mannin!

97. *Spergularia media* **(L.) C. Presl**   **Greater Sea-spurrey, Cabróis mhara mhór**

Saltmarshes.

Sherkin!, Cape Clear!, Bird!, Badger (NR 1993)!, W & E Calf!, Skeam E!, Heir!, Catalogues!, Sandy!, Quarantine!, Jeremy!, Spanish!, Inishleigh!, Mannin!

98. *Spergularia marina* **(L.) Griseb.**   **Lesser Sea-spurrey, Cabróis mhara bheag**

Saltmarshes and around brackish pools on coastal rocks.

Sherkin!, Cape Clear!, Bird!, Badger!, Calfs!, Carthys!, Long!, Horse!, Skeams!, Heir!, Catalogues!, Sandy!, Spanish!, Inishleigh!, Mannin!

99. *Spergularia rubra* **(L.) J. & C. Presl**   **Sand Spurrey, Cabróis dhuimhche**

Cape Clear (Sharrock 1965).

A plant of open, sandy ground. The record might refer to Rock Sea-spurrey, which occurs on Cape Clear at the base of walls away from the sea. However, Sand Spurrey does occur in at least one of the car-parks in Baltimore (JRA & RF 1993), and Colgan & Scully (1898) gave records from Schull and Skibbereen. It is a very local plant in Ireland.

100. *Lychnis flos-cuculi* **L.**   **Ragged Robin, Lus síoda**

Damp fields, marshy ground and beside streams, mostly on the larger islands.

Sherkin!, Cape Clear!, Heir!, Sandy!, Spanish!

[*101. *Agrostemma githago* **L.**   **Corn Cockle, Cogal**

Formerly in cultivated fields. **Irish Red Data Book - Extinct.**

Sherkin (Polunin 1949).

Allin (1883) noted that this species was frequent in cultivated fields in Co. Cork. It was reported in cornfields by Polunin (1949), including "in wheat above Trabawn Bay" (OP, unpublished notes), but not thought worthy of inclusion in Polunin (1950). R. Ll. Praeger, however, stated at about the same that it was "becoming rare in Ireland" (Praeger 1946), and it is now regarded as extinct (Curtis & McGough 1987).

Corn Cockle seems to have originated in the eastern Mediterranean region and spread to other parts of Europe with agriculture. For centuries it was a contaminent of cereal seeds, persisting via resowing each year rather than forming a seed-bank in the soil (Thompson 1973). Efficient seed-cleaning and modern weed-killers have caused its general decline in Europe during this century.]

102. *Silene vulgaris* **(Moench) Garcke (*S. vulgaris* subsp. *vulgaris*)**

Bladder Campion, Coireán na gcuach

Walls, banks and waste ground.

Sherkin!, Cape Clear!, M Calf (LCW 1982), Long!, Horse!, Heir!, Mannin!

Some plants are intermediate between Bladder Campion and Sea Campion.

103. *Silene uniflora* **Roth (*S. vulgaris* subsp. *maritima* (With.) A. & D. Löve**

Sea Campion, Coireán mara

Seashores, shingle beaches and sea-cliffs.

Sherkin!, Cape Clear!, W & M Calf!, Goat!, Little Goat!, Long!, Skeam E (LCW 1982), Heir!, Catalogues!, Spanish!, Mannin!

104. *Silene latifolia* **Poiret subsp. *alba* Greuter & Burdet (*S. alba* (Miller) E.H.L. Krause**

White Campion, Coireán bán

Occasional on disturbed ground.

Sherkin!

A rather scarce plant in Ireland, mostly eastern in distribution.

105. *Silene dioica* **(L.) Clairv.**   **Red Campion, Coireán coilleach**

Locally widespread amongst bracken, by walls, waysides and field borders on Cape Clear; cultivated in gardens on Long.

Cape Clear (mostly at western end)!

Rather common in places at the western end of Cape Clear, where it has been known for a long time (RAP 1896; O'Donovan & O'Regan 1952), although absent from Sherkin and the other islands. A rare plant in Ireland, found mainly in the north, despite being common in Britain. The Cape Clear plants were reddish in all their parts and there was no evidence of the introgressive hybridisation with White Campion that is so characteristic of the species over much of its British range (Baker 1954). It also occurs at Castlefreke, West Cork.

[106. *Silene gallica* **L. (*S. anglica* L.)**   **Small-flowered Catchfly, Coireán Francach**

Weed of cornfields, probably now extinct.

Cape Clear (*O. Polunin 204*, 8.1948, **BM**).

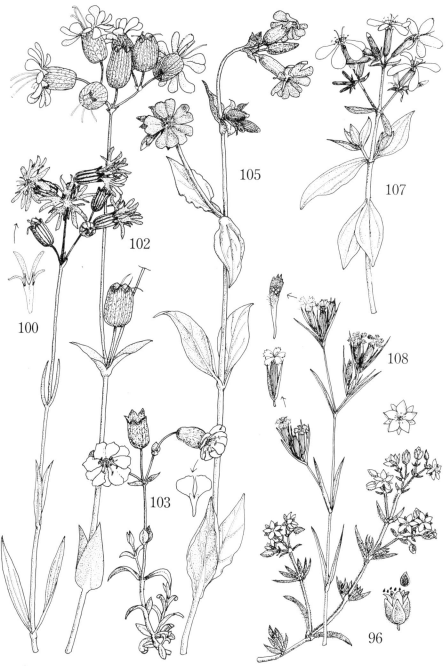

Campion family:

96 Rock Sea-spurrey

100 Ragged Robin

102 Bladder Campion

103 Sea Campion

105 Red Campion

107 Soapwort

108 Deptford Pink

Formerly frequent on the adjacent mainland, especially around Schull (Phillips in Colgan & Scully 1898, Praeger 1901). Once a widespread annual weed of cultivated land, today this is a rare plant in Ireland, as in many parts of Britain.]

*107. *Saponaria officinalis* **L.**   **Soapwort, Garbhán creagach**

Occasionally forming patches on roadsides, by walls and hedges, as an escape from cultivation.

Sherkin!, Cape Clear!, Heir!

The plants on Sherkin and Heir all have double pink flowers. Also known from Schull (RAP 1896) and Baltimore (RAP 1896, JRA 1995).

108. *Dianthus armeria* **L.**   **Deptford Pink, Lus gile Deptford**

One station in south-facing, coastal rocky grassland.

Horse (E. end, JRA & KC 1992)!

Discovered in 1992 as an apparently native plant new to Ireland (Akeroyd & Clarke 1993), this is the only wild Pink in the Irish flora. A subsequent herbarium search also revealed a single specimen from mainland Co. Cork: "a field near The Ovens, Cork (perhaps introduced)", *Herbert Jacob* (Herbarium Isaac Carroll, **BM**). The specimen was correctly labelled and represented a fragment of a large plant. The locality, just north of Cork City, not far from the sea, is reasonable for this species.

Six plants were found on Horse Island in an area of some 12 x 3 m on a south-facing grassy slope, beside outcrops of Old Red Sandstone, severely grazed by sheep and goats (nine plants in 1993; six in 1994, slightly south-west of the original site, PCH & MWR). The site is adjacent to old copper workings. Deptford Pink is widespread but very local in grasslands on sandy soils over much of southern and central Britain, but has decreased in recent years (Perring & Walters 1976, Stace 1991). Studies in Britain have indicated that grazing and trampling by cattle favours the survival of the plant in tall, dense pasture (Wells 1967). Seed production can be high and there is some dormancy, so a reasonable seed-bank may be present on Horse.

The species has a wide distribution in Europe, extending northwards to southern Norway and westwards to Galicia, Cornwall and mid-Wales (Jalas & Suominen 1986), although it is local over much of its range (D.E. Coombe pers. comm.).

NYMPHAEACEAE - waterlilies

109. *Nymphaea alba* **L.**   **White Water-lily, Bacán bán**

Open water of loughs.

Sherkin (Lough Ordree, confirming record of Polunin 1949)!, Cape Clear (Central Bog, OP, unpublished notes; Edmunds 1960).

One of Ireland's most handsome wild flowers, happily still widespread in the west; it occurs on the adjacent mainland.

RANUNCULACEAE – buttercups and water-crowfoots

These plants are an important group in the flora of the islands, growing in grassland and wet places. The buttercups, celandines and spearworts have yellow flowers; the water-crowfoots, which grow in water and on damp mud, have white flowers.

110. *Ranunculus repens* L.   **Creeping Buttercup, Fearbán**

Common in damp grassland, road-verges and disturbed ground.

Sherkin!, Cape Clear!, Calfs!, Carthys!, Goat!, Long!, Castle!, Horse!, Skeams!, Heir!, Catalogues!, Sandy!, Quarantine!, Spanish!, Inishleigh!, Mannin!

111. *Ranunculus acris* L.   **Meadow Buttercup, Fearbán féir**

Grassland and marshy ground.

Sherkin!, Cape Clear!, Calfs!, Carthys (LCW 1982), Goat!, Long!, Castle (LCW 1982), Horse!, Skeams!, Heir!, Catalogues!, Sandy!, Spanish!, Inishleigh!, Mannin!

112. *Ranunculus bulbosus* L.   **Bulbous Buttercup, Tuile thalún**

Coastal grassland and (rarely) as a weed of cultivation; local but undoubtedly under-recorded due to its early flowering season.

Sherkin!, M Calf!, Horse!, Heir!, Sandy!, Spanish!

Readily distinguished by the downward-directed sepals and the bulb-like corm or swelling at the base of the stem. In Ireland this plant is mostly coastal, although it occurs inland on the drier soils of eiscirs (ridges of glacial debris). All Irish plants examined by JRA, including those from Sherkin, have whitish, spreading hairs on the stems and petioles, and have been called var. *dunense* Druce. Similar plants are characteristic of coastal grassland in Britain and drier inland grasslands in England and northern Europe.

113. *Ranunculus sceleratus* L.   **Celery-leaved Buttercup, Toircheas fiáin**

Occasional on wet ground at the margins of pools.

Sherkin!, Cape Clear!, E Calf!, Goat (NR 1993)!, Horse!

Rather a local plant in Ireland; rarer in the west.

114. *Ranunculus ficaria* L.   **Lesser Celandine, Grán arcáin**

Banks, lanesides and damp, shady places. Flowering February to May.

Sherkin!, Cape Clear!, E Calf!, Carthys!, Goat!, Heir!, Sandy!

Flowering early, so often overlooked by botanists. All the plants examined belong to subsp. *ficaria*, which lacks bulbils in the leaf-angles and sets good fruit. It is the commoner of the two Irish subspecies; almost all plants from Co. Cork belong to this subspecies (O'Mahony 1975).

115. *Ranunculus flammula* L.   **Lesser Spearwort, Glasair léana bheag**

Often abundant in marshes, bogs and damp fields.

Sherkin!, Cape Clear!, Calfs!, Goat!, Long!, Castle!, Horse!, Skeams!, Heir!, Catalogues!, Sandy!, Spanish!, Inishleigh!, Mannin!

116. *Ranunculus hederaceus* L.   **Ivy-leaved Water-crowfoot, Néal uisce eidhneach**

Damp mud, especially paths and places trampled by cattle.

Sherkin!, Cape Clear (Edmunds 1960), M & E Calf!, Long!, Castle!, Horse!, Skeam E!, Mannin (LCW 1982).

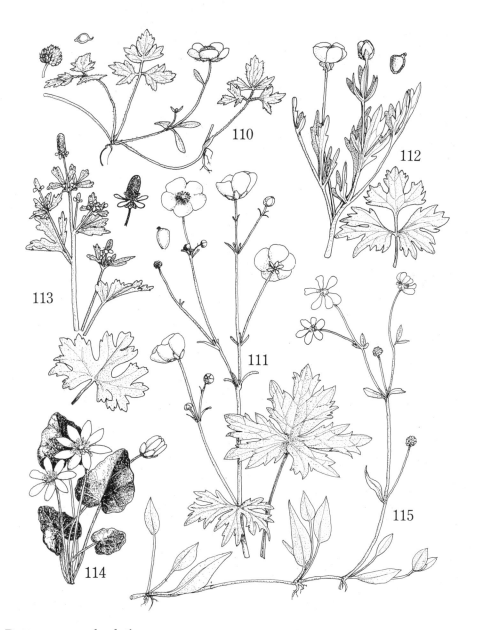

Buttercups and relatives:

110 Creeping Buttercup

111 Meadow Buttercup

112 Bulbous Buttercup

113 Celery-leaved Buttercup

114 Lesser Celandine

115 Lesser Spearwort

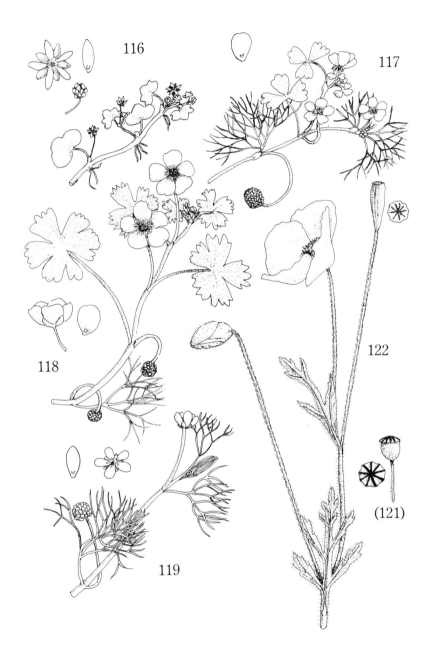

Water-crowfoots and Poppies:

116 Ivy-leaved Water-crowfoot

117 Brackish Water-crowfoot

118 Common Water-crowfoot

119 Thread-leaved Water-crowfoot

(121 Common Poppy)

122 Long-headed Poppy

Marram Grass on blown sand at Silver Strand, Sherkin. Cape Clear is in the background.

The daisy-like flowers of Sea Mayweed provide splashes of colour by the seaside in summer.

Photo: Paul Kay

The familiar spiky leaves and flowerheads of Common Thistle are to be seen along waysides throughout the islands.

Sea Radish, usually a plant of sandy strands, carpets one of the Carthys.

The elegant Bog Pimpernel is frequent in damp places.

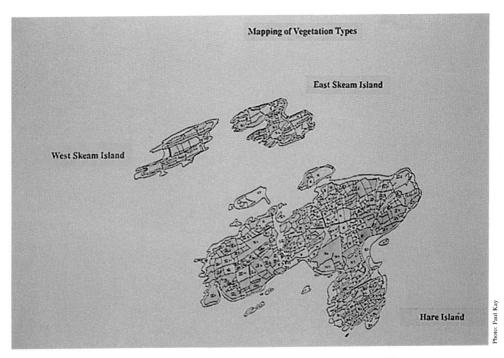

The Vegetation of the islands of Roaringwater Bay: Heir and The Skeams

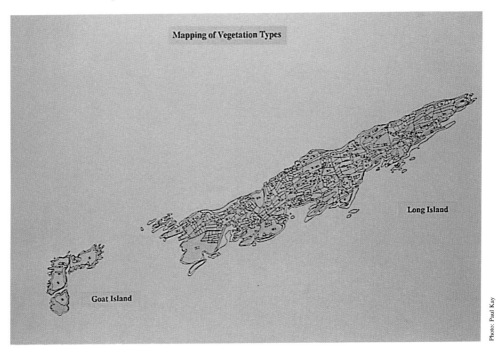

The Vegetation of the islands of Roaringwater Bay: Long and Goat.

The vibrant flowers of Montbretia and other garden escapes give an exotic feel to the islands.

Branched Bur-reed, with its unusual flower structures, grow in wet pastures and beside loughs.

Photo: Ian Watts

Photo: Ian Watts

Photo: Paul Kay

The white seed-heads of cottongrass and the dark red flowers of Marsh Cinquefoil are characteristic features of wet bogs.

Silver Strand, Sherkin, with the Marine Station in the background.

One of the first spring flowers, Common Scurvy-grass brightens cliff-tops and coastal rocks from March to May

The diminutive Round-leaved Sundew, an inhabitant of the wettest bogs, traps insects with the sticky hairs on its leaves.

Kidney Vetch is to be found commonly in grassy and rocky places near the sea.

The stately white trumpets of Easter Lilies grace many an island garden.

The fragrant flowers of Honeysuckle adorn roadside banks in the islands.

Thrift, a familiar plant of cliffs and coastal rocks.

Ragged Robin favours damp meadows.

Photo: Paul Kay

Wild Thyme brightens rocky ground in summer.

Photo: Paul Kay

Striking flowerheads crown the tall stems of Babington's Leek, a relic of ancient Celtic vegetable gardens.

Photo: Paul Kay

The appearance of Common Dog-violet in heaths and grassy banks is a sign that spring has arrived in the islands.

Trabawn, Sherkin Island, showing the reed swamp behind the strand.

The prickly Sea Holly grows in a hostile environment among the sand, rocks and pebbles of the strand.

Photo: Paul Kay

Photo: Paul Kay

The curious fleshy leaves of Wall Pennywort
are a feature of walls and cliffs.

The elegant white spires of Autumn
Lady's-tresses appear as summer ends.

Photo: Paul Kay

Shingle strands are a home for many plants, like this Field Bindweed on Sherkin.

Dwarf Gorse and Bell Heather colour the landscape in late summer.

Pollen preserved in Lough Ordree shows that White Water-Lily has survived on Sherkin since the Ice Age.

Pool at Tramore, Sherkin, with Yellow Flag and other marsh plants.

South Harbour, Cape Clear, is surrounded by rocky heathland.

Bird's-foot Trefoil is one of the prettiest and most abundant grassland flowers.

117. *Ranunculus baudotii* **Godron**   **Brackish Water-crowfoot, Néal uisce sáile**

Slightly brackish pools near the sea.

Sherkin (Tramore, confirming record of Polunin 1949)!, Cape Clear (W. end, Foiladda, *O. Polunin 212*, [1947-48] **BM**), W Calf (NR 1993)!, E Calf (PCH & MWR 1994, confirming record of Allin 1883)!, Long!

Regarded by many continental botanists as a subspecies of Pond Water-crowfoot (*R. peltatus* Schrank), but quite distinct from that species in the British Isles. A rather scarce plant in Ireland, but locally common in places on western coasts.

118. *Ranunculus aquatilis* **L.**   **Common Water-crowfoot, Néal uisce coiteann**

Pools.

Sherkin (Trabawn, NS 1992), M Calf!, E Calf (LCW 1982, PCH & MWR 1994)!, Long (LCW 1982).

119. *Ranunculus trichophyllus* **Chaix**

Thread-leaved Water-crowfoot, Néal uisce ribeach

Pools and loughs.

Sherkin!, Cape Clear (Sharrock 1965), E Calf!, Long!

PAPAVERACEAE – poppies

*120. *Papaver somniferum* **L.**   **Opium Poppy, Codlaidín**

Waste ground; garden escape.

Sherkin (JRA & DAW 1987), Cape Clear (Sharrock 1965).

121. *Papaver rhoeas* **L.**   **Common Poppy, Cailleach dhearg**

Rare on cultivated and waste ground and sometimes on the upper part of strands.

Sherkin!, Cape Clear!, Horse!

122. *Papaver dubium* **L.**   **Long-headed Poppy, Cailleach fhada**

Occasional on cultivated and disturbed ground, and the upper part of strands.

Sherkin (Horseshoe Harbour, JRA & SLJ 1986; near the Castle; several stations between Cow Strand and the Marine Station)!, Heir!

Polunin (1950) recorded this species "sparingly" in cornfields; today it is the commoner poppy on Sherkin. Both Common Poppy and Long-headed Poppy have declined with the loss of arable land on the islands.

123. *Glaucium flavum* **Crantz**   **Yellow Horned-poppy, Caillichín na trá**

Shingle strands and gravelly ground near the sea; locally abundant.

Sherkin!, M Calf (as *G. luteum*, Allin 1883; T O'M 1992, NR 1993)!, Long!, Castle!, Heir!

FUMARIACEAE – fumitories

Fumitories are all plants of cultivated or disturbed ground. They are especially widespread and variable in West & North-West Europe, with several species, subspecies and varieties restricted to Britain, Ireland and northern France.

124. *Fumaria purpurea* Pugsley   Purple Ramping-fumitory, Camán searraigh corcra

Shingle strands and disturbed ground.

Long (W. end, NR 1993)!, Horse (JRA 1994)!

A rare plant that is of special interest because it occurs only in Ireland and Britain. It is very similar to Pale Ramping-fumitory (*F. capreolatea* L.), but has more purplish petals and slightly larger, more toothed sepals. The fruits of both species have strongly downcurved stalks.

125. *Fumaria bastardii* Boreau   Tall Ramping-fumitory, Camán searraigh ard

Local but sometimes abundant on cultivated ground.

Sherkin!, Cape Clear!, Long!, Horse!, Heir!

Reported by Polunin (1949) to be "locally frequent on cultivated ground". The great majority of plants examined belonged to var. *bastardii*. Var. *hibernica* Pugsley, easily recognised by the blackish-red wings of the upper petals and superficially similar to *F. muralis* subsp. *boraei*, occurs on Sherkin, Heir, Horse and probably elsewhere. It was recorded from a number of places in Kerry by Scully (1916, p.15).

126. *Fumaria muralis* Sonder ex Koch subsp. *boraei* (Jordan) Pugsley

Common Ramping-fumitory, Camán searraigh balla

Local but sometimes abundant on cultivated ground, especially among potatoes; less frequently on waste ground or coastal shingle.

Sherkin!, Cape Clear!, Long!, Castle!, Horse!, Skeam W!, Heir!

Reported from "Potato field, Inisherkin, 1896" by Phillips in Colgan & Scully (1898). Polunin (1950) noted it to be rare, although in 1992-95 it was the commonest fumitory on Sherkin, Cape Clear and Heir. Plants from just south-west of Trabawn Strand (*J.R. Akeroyd & S.L. Jury*, 2.8.86, **RNG**), more slender and with smaller sepals and slightly smaller obovate to subglobose fruits, were determined as var. *britannica* Pugsley by P.D. Sell. This variant, which had not been reported from Ireland in the literature, was still present in 1992 in a potato patch at the same locality (*fide* JRA). Similar plants have been seen on Cape Clear (JRA & NR 1993).

JRA has examined three other Irish specimens, from Killiney, Co. Dublin (*C. Pearson, 24.3.1907*, **TCD**), Saintfield, Co. Down (*C.H. Waddell*, 9.1903, **CGE**) and near Gorey, Co. Wexford (*E.S. Marshall*, 14.6.1897, **BM**), all determined by H.W. Pugsley (1888 - 1947), the acknowledged expert on Irish and British fumitories. In Britain var. *britannica* is widespread and like many fumitories is especially common in south-west England.

127. *Fumaria officinalis* L. subsp. *wirtgenii* (Koch) Arcang.

Common Fumitory, Camán searraigh díge

Rare on cultivated ground.

Sherkin (potato patch above Trabawn Strand)!, Cape Clear!, E Calf!, Heir!

Subsp. *wirtgenii*, distinguished from subsp. *officinalis* by smaller sepals and not more than 20 flowers in each raceme, has been not reported from Ireland in Irish or British floras. However, it is probably the commoner of the two subspecies in Ireland (J.R. Akeroyd & P.D. Sell, unpublished data). Material from Sherkin and Heir apparently all belongs to subsp. *wirtgenii*, although some plants approach subsp. *officinalis*. For a summary of the variation in this and other fumitories, see P.D. Sell's key in Rich & Rich (1988).

Doubtful records of Fine-leaved Fumitory (*F. parviflora* Lam.) from Cape Clear and Three Castles Head were never confirmed even during the 19th century (Allin 1883, Colgan & Scully 1898).

BRASSICACEAE or CRUCIFERAE – cabbages, cresses and mustards

Most members of this family have a 'mustard' flavour, and many were formerly eaten as salads, especially during the winter months when greens were scarce.

128. *Sisymbrium officinale* **(L.) Scop.**   **Hedge Mustard, Lus an óir**

Waysides and disturbed ground.

Sherkin!, Cape Clear!, M Calf!, Long!, Castle!, Horse!, Heir!

129. *Alliaria petiolata* **(Bieb.) Cavara & Grande**   **Garlic Mustard, Bóchoinneal**

Cape Clear (Edmunds 1960).

*130. *Hesperis matronalis* **L.**   **Dame's-violet, Feascarlus**

Waysides near houses, as an occasional escape from cultivation.

Sherkin!, Cape Clear!

Plants with purple, lilac and white petals occur. Noted from near Schull, as a "garden outcast", by Phillips in Praeger (1901).

*131. *Armoracia rusticana* **P. Gaertner, B. Meyer & Scherb.**

                                              Horse-radish, Meacan ragaim

Occasional on waysides or cultivated land.

Sherkin ("close to ruined castle walls", as *Cochlearia armoracia*, Polunin 1949, confirmed MWR 1995; garden at Horseshoe Harbour, JRA & SLJ 1986)!, Long!, Heir!

Easily recognised by the conspicuous clumps of erect, dark green, blunt, dock-like leaves.

132. *Nasturtium officinale* **R.Br.**   **Water-cress, Biolar**

Marshy ground, pools and beside streams and roadside runnels.

Sherkin!, Cape Clear!, M & E Calf!, Long!, Castle!, Horse!, Skeam E!, Heir!, Catalogues!, Sandy (LCW 1982), Spanish!, Mannin (LCW 1992).

Narrow-fruited Water-cress (*N. microphyllum* (Boenn.) Reichenb.), with seeds in a single row, rather than 2 rows, has been reported from East Calf (PSWJ 1979).

133. *Cardamine pratensis* **L.**   **Lady's Smock, Biolar gréagáin**

Locally abundant in marshy places and wet meadows.

Sherkin!, Cape Clear!, Calfs!, Long!, Castle!, Horse!, Skeam E!, Heir!, Catalogues!, Sandy!, Spanish!, Mannin!

A double-flowered variant occurs on Sherkin, Cape Clear and Horse. This was reported from Clare Island, Co. Mayo, by Praeger (1911). Records of Large Bitter-cress (*C. amara*), restricted in Ireland to Ulster, almost certainly refer to pale-flowered variants of this plant.

134.   *Cardamine flexuosa* **With.**   **Wavy Bitter-cress, Searbh-bhiolar casta**

Cultivated ground and around ruins.

Sherkin (garden of Jolly Roger)!, Cape Clear!, E Calf!, Castle!, Horse!, Catalogues (LCW 1982), Sandy!, Inishleigh!, Mannin!

135.   *Cardamine hirsuta* **L.**   **Hairy Bitter-cress, Searbh-bhiolar giobach**

Open and disturbed ground, especially gardens.

Sherkin!, Cape Clear!, E Calf!, Long!, Castle!, Skeam E!, Heir!

136.   *Erophila verna* **(L.) Chevall**   **Spring Whitlowgrass, Bosán anagair**

Rare in open ground, on blown sand over rocks by strand. Flowering March to April.

Sherkin (Cow Strand, PCH 1995)!

Rare in South-Western Ireland and the first record of this plant from West Cork. It flowers early in the spring so may be overlooked in some areas.

137.   *Cochlearia danica* **L.**   **Early Scurvygrass, Carrán creige**

Open stony and rocky places by the sea.

Sherkin!, Cape Clear!, M Calf (T O'M 1992)!, Carthys (BM 1995)!, Castle!

This annual plant flowers early and so is often overlooked.

138.   *Cochlearia officinalis* **L.**   **Common Scurvygrass, Biolar trá**

Frequent on rocks, shingle strands, short turf on sea-cliffs, and bases of walls near the sea; also on bird islands.

Sherkin!, Cape Clear!, Bird!, Badger!, Calfs!, Carthys!, Goat!, Little Goat!, Long!, Castle!, Horse!, Skeams!, Heir!, Catalogues!, Sandy!, Quarantine!, Jeremy!, Spanish!, Inishleigh!, Mannin!

Plants with small, round leaves from Sherkin, East Calf and other islands belong within subsp. *scotica* (Druce) P. Wyse Jackson and are the basis of old records of *C. groenlandica* L., an Arctic species, from here and elsewhere in Western Ireland (P.S. Wyse Jackson, pers. comm.).

139.   *Capsella bursa-pastoris* **(L.) Medicus**   **Shepherd's Purse, Lus an spáráin**

Cultivated ground and waysides.

Sherkin!, Cape Clear!, Calfs!, Long!, Castle!, Horse!, Skeam E!, Heir!, Catalogues (LCW 1982).

140.   *Coronopus squamatus* **(Forsskål) Ascherson**   **Swine-cress, Cladhthach**

Disturbed, bare or trampled ground.

Sherkin!, Cape Clear!, Calfs!, Carthys (*O. Polunin 143*, 8.1948, **BM**), Long!, Castle (LCW 1982), Horse!, Skeam E!, Heir!

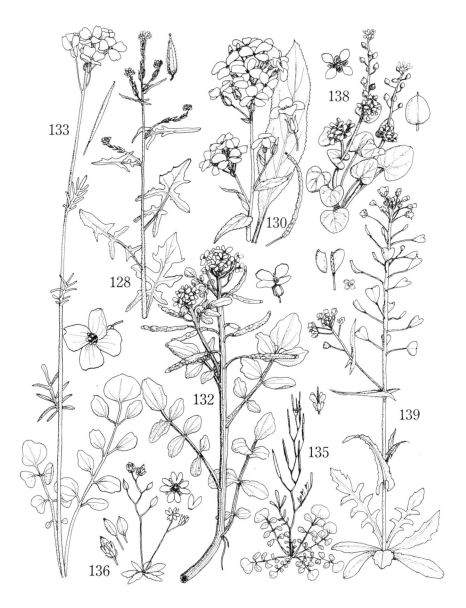

Cabbage and Cress family:

128 Hedge Mustard

130 Dame's-violet

132 Water-cress

133 Lady's Smock

135 Hairy Bitter-cress

136 Spring Whitlowgrass

138 Common Scurvygrass

139 Shepherd's Purse

Cabbage and Cress family:

140 Swine-cress

141 Lesser Swine-cress

142 Wild Turnip

144 Black Mustard

145 Charlock

146 Sea Rocket

147 Sea Kale

148 Sea Radish

*141. *Coronopus didymus* (L.) Sm.   **Lesser Swine-cress, Cladhthach mhín**

Waste ground.

Sherkin (confirming record of Polunin 1949)!, Cape Clear!, Long!, Heir!

142. *Brassica rapa* L. subsp. *campestris* (L.) Clapham   **Wild Turnip, Tornapa fiáin**

Cultivated ground, waysides and earthy sea-cliffs.

Sherkin!, Cape Clear!, Long!, Horse!, Heir!

*143. *Brassica rapa* L. subsp. *oleifera* (DC.) Metzger   **Turnip Rape, Tornapa ráibe**

Cultivated as a fodder crop and sometimes escaping on to waste ground.

Cape Clear (JRA & BM 1995)!

144. *Brassica nigra* (L.) Koch   **Black Mustard, Praiseach dhubh**

Rare in waste places and on roadsides.

Sherkin (confirming record of Polunin 1949)!, M & E Calf (LCW 1982), Horse (KC 1992)!

Also reported, as *Sinapis nigra,* by Allin (1883), beside the River Ilen below Skibbereen.

145. *Sinapis arvensis* L.   **Charlock, Praiseach bhuí**

Cultivated ground and waysides, sometimes in abundance.

Sherkin!, Cape Clear!, Long!, Horse!, Skeam W!, Heir!

Plants on Sherkin, for example in the garden of the Marine Station (JRA 1990-93), and Cape Clear (South Harbour, JRA & BM 1995), have both hairless and hairy fruits; plants with the latter are var. *orientalis* (L.) Koch & Ziz.

146. *Cakile maritima* Scop.   **Sea Rocket, Cearrbhacán mara**

Rare and sporadic on sandy strands.

Sherkin (confirming record of Polunin 1949)!

147. *Crambe maritima* L.   **Sea Kale, Praiseach thrá**

Rare on shingle strands. **Irish Red Data Book - Not Threatened.**

M Calf (PCH & MWR 1994)!

A local plant of coasts in Ireland, formerly decreasing but now apparently stabilised in numbers and known from 17 stations from Kerry to Louth (Curtis & McGough 1988).

148. *Raphanus raphanistrum* L. subsp. *maritimus*   **Sea Radish, Meacan mara**

Locally common in waste places and abandoned fields near the sea, sand and shingle strands.

Sherkin!, Cape Clear (Edmunds 1960, Sharrock 1965), M & E Calf!, Carthys!, Long (confirming record of O'Donovan & O'Regan 1952)!, Castle (confirming record of Allin 1883)!, Horse!, Skeams!, Heir!, Catalogues!, Sandy!, Quarantine!, Spanish!, Inishleigh!

Reported as "abundant" on Sherkin and Heir by Phillips (RAP 1902); both Polunin (1949) and O'Donovan & O'Regan (1952) recorded plants at Tranaplousa [Silver Strand]. The species is today widespread in the islands, although generally scarce in Co. Cork and Kerry (see Scully 1916). Some white-flowered plants occur with the commoner yellow-flowered variant at Silver and Cow Strands. Also reported from near Goleen (O'Donovan & O'Regan 1952) and on Sheeps Head (T. O'Mahony, pers. comm.).

RESEDACEAE - mignonettes

*149. *Reseda luteola* **L.**   **Weld, Buí mór**

Disturbed ground; probably introduced with wildflower seed or earth-moving machinery.

Cape Clear (above South Harbour, JRA & BM 1995)!

A characteristic plant of new road verges and other open ground. It is widespread in Ireland but scarce in Co. Cork. A yellow dye is obtained from this plant.

DROSERACEAE - sundews

150. *Drosera rotundifolia* **L.**   **Round-leaved Sundew, Drúchtín móna**

Local in bogs; the commonest of the insect-trapping plants.

Sherkin!, Cape Clear!, Spanish!

CRASSULACEAE - stonecrops

151. *Umbilicus rupestris* **(Salisb.) Dandy   Wall Pennywort or Navelwort, Cornán caisil**

Common on stone walls, abandoned buildings and rock outcrops.

Sherkin!, Cape Clear!, Calfs!, Goat!, Long!, Castle!, Horse!, Skeams!, Heir!, Catalogues!, Sandy!, Quarantine!, Jeremy!, Spanish!, Inishleigh!, Mannin!

152. *Sedum anglicum* **Hudson**   **White or English Stonecrop, Póiríní seangán**

Rock outcrops and wall-tops.

Sherkin!, Cape Clear!, Calfs!, Carthys!, Goat!, Little Goat!, Long!, Castle!, Horse!, Skeams!, Heir!, Catalogues!, Sandy!, Quarantine!, Jeremy!, Spanish!, Inishleigh!, Mannin!
  Two other stonecrops have been reported from Cape Clear: Biting Stonecrop (*S. acre* L.) needs confirmation, but Hairy Stonecrop (*S. villosum* L.) is probably an error.

SAXIFRAGACEAE – saxifrages

153. *Saxifraga spathularis* **Brot.   St Patrick's Cabbage, Cabáiste an mhadra rua**

Rare on damp, mossy rocks.

Sherkin (near S.E. side of Horseshoe Harbour, PCH & MWR 1994)!

Although not previously reported from the islands, this West and South-West European plant has its Irish headquarters in Co. Cork and Kerry. It is one of the 15 Irish plants that do not occur in Britain.

154. *Chrysosplenium oppositifolium* L.   **Opposite-leaved Golden-saxifrage, Glóiris**

Damp, shady streamsides and roadside runnels.

Sherkin!, Cape Clear!, Horse!, Spanish!

ESCALLONIACEAE - escallonias

*155. *Escallonia rubra* **(Ruiz & Pavon) Pers. var.** *macrantha* **(Hooker & Arnott) Reiche**

Escallonia, Tomóg ghlaech

Frequently planted in gardens and as a hedge on the larger islands; long introduced from temperate South America. Also in hedges on Ringarogy Island (JRA & DAW 1987).

Sherkin!, Cape Clear!, Horse!, Heir!

GROSSULARIACEAE – currants

*156. *Ribes rubrum* **L. (***R. sylvestre* **(Lam.) Mert. & Koch)   Red Currant, Cuirín dearg**

Heir!

A garden escape in Ireland, although perhaps native in damp woodlands in Britain. Kelly (1985) reports Irish records from wooded islands in loughs, but these are likely to be bird-sown.

*157. *Ribes nigrum* **L.**   **Black Currant, Cuirín dubh**

Occasional in scrub and hedges, an escape from gardens.

Sherkin!, Heir!

Like Red Currant, not native in Ireland, but perhaps so in Britain. O'Mahony (1975) notes a few records from wet woods in Mid & East Cork.

*158. *Ribes uva-crispa* **L.**   **Gooseberry, Spíonán**

Rare in scrub, an escape from gardens.

Cape Clear (confirming record of Edmunds 1960)!, Skeam E!

Not native in Ireland but rather infrequently naturalised (O'Mahony 1975).

ROSACEAE – cinquefoils, roses and related species

A varied family with a range of fruit structures. Roses and fruits such as apples and strawberries are grown widely in gardens.

159. *Filipendula ulmaria* **(L.) Maxim.**   **Meadowsweet, Airgead luachra**

Rather local in marshes, damp fields and lanesides.

Sherkin!, Cape Clear!, Long!, Horse!, Heir!, Sandy!, Spanish!, Inishleigh!

160. *Rubus ulmifolius* **Schott**   **Blackberry or Bramble, Dris**

Heathland, hedges, stone walls and abandoned fields.

Sherkin!, Cape Clear!, Calfs!, Long!, Castle!, Horse!, Skeams!, Heir!, Catalogues!, Sandy!, Quarantine!, Jeremy!, Spanish!, Inishleigh!, Mannin!

Brambles can be divided into numerous 'microspecies' based on tiny differences. There is, however, apparently only one bramble on the islands, very spiny but with succulent, edible fruits. This has been identified by D.E. Allen, who noted that this bramble is "seemingly impervious to salt-laden winds, so it tends to dominate in coastal areas south of Scotland". It is the common hedgerow bramble in Kerry (P.S. Wyse Jackson, pers. comm.).

161. *Rosa pimpinellifolia* **L.**   **Burnet Rose, Briúlán**

Rare on rocky banks and heathy ground.

Sherkin (by road above Trabawn; Foardree, KC 1992)!, Cape Clear (confirming records held at Bird Observatory)!, Horse!

***162.** *Rosa rugosa* **Thunb.**   **Japanese Rose, Rós rúscach**

Escaping from gardens on to roadside banks.

Cape Clear!

163. *Rosa canina* **L.**   **Dog Rose, Feirdhris**

Hedges and scrub. A.L. Primavesi has identified collections from Sherkin as this species.

Sherkin!, Cape Clear!, Castle!, Horse!, Heir!, Spanish!

Another wild rose, Small-flowered Sweet-briar (*R. micrantha* Sm.), has been recorded from Schull (RAP 1896) and maritime heathland on Ringarogy Island (JRA & DAW 1987). This is a rare species in Ireland, but has several records from the south-west, including Co. Cork (Allin 1883) and Kerry (Scully 1916). It may occur in the islands.

164. *Geum urbanum* **L.**   **Wood Avens, Machall coille**

Damp, shady places.

Spanish!

165. *Potentilla palustris* **(L.) Scop.**   **Marsh Cinquefoil, Cnó léana**

Marshes and boggy places.

Sherkin!, Cape Clear!, M Calf!, Long!, Heir!, Spanish!

166. *Potentilla anserina* **L.**   **Silverweed, Briosclán**

Abundant on upper part of strands, especially amongst pebbles; also trampled pastures, tracksides and waste ground around houses and ruins.

Sherkin!, Cape Clear!, Badger!, Calfs!, Carthys!, Goat!, Long!, Castle!, Horse!, Skeams!, Heir!, Catalogues!, Sandy!, Quarantine!, Jeremy!, Spanish!, Inishleigh!, Mannin!

The fleshy roots were formerly widely eaten in Ireland and Scotland, and may even have been a cultivated crop.

167. *Potentilla erecta* **(L.) Rauschel**   **Tormentil, Néalfartach**

Abundant on roadsides and heathy grassland.

Sherkin!, Cape Clear!, Calfs!, Goat!, Long!, Castle!, Horse!, Skeams!, Heir!, Catalogues!, Sandy!, Quarantine!, Jeremy!, Spanish!, Inishleigh!, Mannin!

168. *Potentilla anglica* Laicharding   **Trailing Tormentil, Néalfartach shraoilleach**

Occasional on roadside banks.

Sherkin (BM 1995, confirming record, as *P. procumbens*, of Polunin 1950)!, Cape Clear!, E Calf (PSWJ 1979), Castle!, Skeam E!, Mannin!

Trailing Tormentil and its hybrids with Tormentil and Creeping Cinquefoil are probably under-recorded in the islands. A specimen from Horse (MQ 1975), with a straggling habit and stalked leaves with 3-4 leaflets, is close to the hybrid with Tormentil, *P. x suberecta* Zimm.

169. *Potentilla anglica x reptans* (*P. x mixta* Nolte ex Reichenb.)

Sherkin (as *P. procumbens x reptans*, Polunin 1950), Long (BM & MWR 1995)!, Skeam E (BM 1995)!, Heir (BM & MWR 1995)!, Mannin (BM 1995)!

This hybrid, which is less robust than Creeping Cinquefoil, and has leaves with 3-4 leaflets and some flowers with 3-4 petals, is widespread in Ireland and Britain and may have been overlooked elsewhere in the islands, as suggested by the recent records of B. Milner.

170. *Potentilla reptans* L.   **Creeping Cinquefoil, Cúig mhéar Mhuire**

Dry banks and lanesides; stony, waste ground.

Sherkin!, Cape Clear!, Long!, Horse!, Skeams!, Heir!

171. *Potentilla sterilis* (L.) Garcke   **Barren Strawberry, Sú talún bréige**

Local on dry banks and in the shade of bracken and scrub.

Sherkin!, Cape Clear (Polunin, unpublished notes; Edmunds 1960), Spanish!

172. *Fragaria vesca* L.   **Wild Strawberry, Sú talún fiáin**

Amongst bracken.

Spanish!

173. *Aphanes arvensis* L. (*Alchemilla arvensis* L.)   **Parsley-piert, Mionán Muire**

Bare ground, tracks and rocky fields.

Sherkin!, Cape Clear!, M Calf!, Long!, Castle!, Skeam E!, Heir!

*174. *Malus domestica* Borkh.   **Apple, Abhaill**

Hedges and scrub, probably from discarded apple cores.

Sherkin!, Skeam E (JRA & NR 1993)!, Heir (JS 1990)!

*175. *Cotoneaster simonsii* Baker   **Himalayan Cotoneaster, Cainchín Áiseach**

Occasional but widely scattered in hedges and on road verges; an escape from gardens, sown by birds which feed on the berries.

Sherkin!

176. *Crataegus monogyna* **Jacq.**   **Hawthorn, Sceach gheal**

Common in hedges and scrub.

Sherkin!, Cape Clear!, Horse!, Heir!, Spanish!, Mannin!

177. *Prunus spinosa* **L.**   **Blackthorn, Draighean**

Common in scrub and hedges; often forming impenetrable thickets.

Sherkin!, Cape Clear!, E Calf!, Long!, Castle!, Horse!, Skeam E!, Heir!, Spanish!

The traditional source of the countryman's stick. The fruits are sloes.

LEGUMINOSAE – clovers, trefoils and vetches

Members of this family ('legumes') are very important plants of grassland. Several of the wild clovers, vetches and other legumes are cultivated as forage plants. The wild plants are thus an important potential genetic resource.

*178. *Laburnum anagyroides* **Medicus**   **Laburnum, Beallaí francach**

Hedge.

Sherkin (near Jolly Rodger, KC 1992)!

179. *Cytisus scoparius* **(L.) Link subsp.** *scoparius*   **Broom, Giolcach shléibhe**

Rare on south-facing slopes, usually near the sea.

Sherkin (Foardree)!, Cape Clear (South Harbour and elsewhere, confirming unpublished OP record)!

180. *Ulex europaeus* **L.**   **Gorse or French Gorse, Aiteann gallda**

Abundant on heaths and abandoned pastures, in hedgerows and along walls, often forming dense thickets.

Sherkin!, Cape Clear!, Calfs!, Carthys!, Long!, Castle!, Horse!, Skeams!, Heir!, Catalogues!, Sandy!, Jeremy!, Spanish!, Inishleigh!, Mannin!

Formerly of enormous importance to the rural economy of the islands and Ireland generally: kindling and fuel for ovens, fodder and bedding for animals, hedging, thatch, even as a primitive harrow and as a brush for sweeping chimneys (Lucas 1960, O'Reilly 1994). It flowers throughout the year but mostly in spring. The flowers smell sweetly of vanilla.

181. *Ulex gallii* **Planchon**   **Western or Irish Gorse, Aiteann gaelach**

Abundant and often dominant in dry heathland.

Sherkin!, Cape Clear!, Calfs!, Goat!, Long!, Castle!, Horse!, Skeams!, Heir!, Catalogues!, Sandy!, Quarantine!, Jeremy!, Spanish!, Inishleigh!, Mannin!

Widely used, but of less economic importance than 'French' (sometimes known as 'English') Gorse. This plant brightens heaths and rocky ground with its flowers in late summer.

*182. *Lupinus angustifolius* **L.**   **Narrow-leaved Lupin, Lúipín caol**

Disturbed ground; probably introduced with wildflower seed.

Cape Clear (above South Harbour, JRA & BM 1995)!

183. *Vicia cracca* L.   Tufted Vetch, Peasair na luch

Common in tall grassland, hedges and sometimes on sea-cliffs.

Sherkin!, Cape Clear!, Calfs!, Long!, Castle!, Horse!, Skeams!, Heir!, Spanish!, Inishleigh!, Mannin!

184. *Vicia hirsuta* (L.) S.F. Gray   Hairy Tare, Peasair arbhair

Waysides and grassy banks; formerly in arable fields.

Sherkin (Polunin 1949; between Post Office and Castle, FAB 1981, JRA 1990, MWR 1995; Kinish Harbour, BM 1995)!, Cape Clear (North Harbour, PCH & MWR 1994, confirming record of Edmunds 1960)!, Long!, Horse!, Heir!

185. *Vicia sepium* L.   Bush Vetch, Peasair fhiáin

Roadsides, hedges and sea-cliffs.

Sherkin!, Cape Clear!, Long!, Castle!, Horse!, Skeam W!, Heir!, Spanish!

Some plants at the western end of Cape Clear have cream flowers (var. *ochroleuca* Bast.). JRA has seen an early 20th century specimen of this variant from near Letterkenny, Co. Donegal (*F.R. Browning*, G.C. Druce's Herbarium, **OXF**). It is scattered in Britain.

*186. *Vicia sativa* L. subsp. *segetalis* (Thuill.) Gaudin Common Vetch, Peasair chapaill

Common on road-verges, waste areas, cultivated land, sometimes on shingle strands, often near habitations.

Sherkin!, Cape Clear!, M & W Calf!, Goat!, Long!, Castle!, Horse!, Skeams!, Heir!, Quarantine!, Jeremy!, Inishleigh!

Variable, with some robust plants from Sherkin (for example, *F.A. Bisby 1471*, 31.7.81, **STH**), Heir and Cape Clear being probably referable to subsp. *sativa*, representing a relic of a former fodder crop. Polunin (1949) noted it as an escape from cultivation, but well established. Records from Sherkin and Long of Spring Vetch (*V. lathyroides*) L., a rare plant of the coasts of south-east Ireland, are based on diminutive plants of subsp. *segetalis* (*fide* JRA).

187. *Vicia sativa* L. subsp. *nigra* (L.) Ehrh. (*V. angustifolia* L.)

Narrow-leaved Vetch, Peasair chaol

Sherkin (Polunin 1949; Silver Strand, LCW 1982).

188. *Lathyrus japonicus* Willd. subsp. *maritimus* (L.) P.W. Ball (*L. maritimus* Bigel.)

Sea Pea, Peasairín trá

Rare on shingle strands. **Irish Red Data Book - Indeterminate.**

Castle (BM & MWR 1995)!, Heir (BM & MWR 1995)!

These two Roaringwater Bay records are an important extension of this plant's known range. Locally common on shingle in parts of South-East England, this handsome peaflower is restricted in Ireland to four western sites: two in Kerry and one in Donegal (with another in West Mayo destroyed in a storm), and a 1992 West Cork record from Clonakilty (O'Mahony 1994). It is an enigmatic plant in Ireland - the seeds may drift here from North America.

189. *Lathyrus montanus* **Bernh.**   **Bitter Vetch, Corra meille**

Rare on heathy banks.

Long!, Inishleigh!

190. *Lathyrus pratensis* **L.**   **Meadow Vetchling, Peasairín buí**

Roadsides and damp meadows.

Sherkin!, Cape Clear!, Calfs!, Long!, Castle!, Horse!, Skeams!, Heir!, Spanish!, Inishleigh!, Mannin!

*191. *Lathyrus latifolius* **L.**   **Broad-leaved Everlasting-pea, Peasairín leathan**

Garden escape, growing in hedges.

Sherkin!, Heir!

Plants from near the school on Heir have white flowers (cultivar 'Albus').

192. *Ononis repens* **L.**   **Creeping Restharrow, Fréamhacha tairne**

Local in rough coastal grassland.

Sherkin (near The Dock)!, E Calf (confirming records of *O. Polunin 117*, 8.1948, **BM**; KRB 1985)!, Long!, Heir!

A scarce plant in western Ireland. O'Donovan & O'Regan (1952), however, noted that derelict fields on Sherkin were covered with mats of this plant.

193. *Medicago lupulina* **L.**   **Black Medick, Dúmheidic**

Grassland and road-verges; often on grassy walls near the sea.

Sherkin!, Cape Clear!, M & E Calf!, Horse!, Skeams!, Heir!

A robust, larger-flowered agricultural variant occurs here and there on Sherkin.

194. *Trifolium ornithopodioides* **L.**   **Bird's-foot Clover, Seamair éin**

Rare in dry, open ground and rocky grassland; also stone-flagged quays.

Sherkin (Horseshoe Harbour, RF 1993; JRA, PCH & MWR 1994)!, Cape Clear (North Harbour, O'Donovan 1953; JRA 1994-5)!

Also recorded on and around the pier at Baltimore (O'Donovan 1953) and more recently found on Ringarogy Island (Wyse Jackson 1995). The only other station in Co. Cork is near James Fort, Kinsale (*T. O'Mahony et al.*, 22.5.76, **DBN**).

195. *Trifolium repens* **L.**   **White or Dutch Clover, Seamair bhán**

Abundant in grassland and on waysides and open ground.

Sherkin!, Cape Clear!, Calfs!, Carthys!, Goat!, Little Goat!, Long!, Castle!, Horse!, Skeams!, Heir!, Catalogues!, Sandy!, Quarantine!, Jeremy!, Spanish!, Inishleigh!, Mannin!

*196. *Trifolium hybridum* **L.**   **Alsike Clover, Seamair Lochlannach**

Cape Clear (Edmunds 1960 and records held at Bird Observatory).

Scully (1916, p.67) has a note on its occurrence via agricultural improvement in Kerry, surviving as an escape from cultivation.

197. *Trifolium campestre* **Schreber**   **Hop Trefoil, Seamair dhuimhche**

Rare on rocky banks and dry grassland; sometimes on grassy wall-tops.

Sherkin (near Silver Strand, confirming record of Polunin 1949)!, Horse (E. end, RF 1993; MWR 1994)!, Catalogues (PCH & MWR 1994)!

On Sherkin apparently restricted to a small area, where it has been repeatedly observed since it was refound by P. Whelan in 1975. Somewhat lime-loving, it probably benefits from the shell-content of the blown sand at this site. The new records are encouraging.

198. *Trifolium dubium* **Sibth.**   **Lesser Trefoil or Suckling Clover, Seamair bhuí**

Common in short, dry grassland, and on rocky banks and grassy walls near the sea; often on anthills. This clover is commonly sold as Shamrock.

Sherkin!, Cape Clear!, Calfs!, Carthys (LCW 1982), Goat!, Long!, Castle!, Horse!, Skeams!, Heir!, Catalogues!, Sandy!, Spanish!, Inishleigh!, Mannin!

199. *Trifolium micranthum* **Viv. (***T. filiforme* **L.)**   **Slender Trefoil, Seamair bheag**

Local in short grassland over sand or rocks near the sea.

Sherkin!, M Calf (PCH & MWR 1994)!, Long (MWR 1994)!, Horse (JRA 1994)!, Skeam E (PCH & MWR 1994)!, Heir (PCH 1994)!

First reported by Polunin (1949, 1950), new to West Cork, and refound (JRA 1986, 1994) in the grounds of Sherkin Marine Island Station, by the Lighthouse (JRA & DAW 1987) and at Horseshoe Harbour (JRA, PCH & MWR 1994); also on Ringarogy Island (JRA & DAW 1987, Wyse Jackson 1995). The many recent records suggest that this diminutive clover should be looked for elsewhere, despite the pessimistic view of Allin (1883), who dismissed all records of this species and Soft Clover from Co. Cork! Scully (1916) gives several records from Kerry.
     Hart (1899) suggested that in Co. Donegal at least it might have been introduced with grass-seed. The slightly orange tint to the flowers is distinctive.

200. *Trifolium striatum* **L.**   **Soft Clover, Seamair stríocach**

Rare on rock outcrops, dry banks and grassy walls near the sea.

Sherkin (scattered stations between Post Office and Horseshoe Harbour)!

First recorded on Sherkin in July 1976 by O'Mahony (1979), who noted "a few plants" on rocky hedgebanks at the road junction above the harbour on Sherkin. Since 1986 JRA has found small populations on rock outcrops between here and Horseshoe Harbour, which were still there in 1994, but has failed to relocate the clover at the road junction. There has been some reconstruction of walls and a new telephone kiosk has been erected, which may have destroyed the plant's habitat. This clover is mostly eastern in distribution in Ireland, but has three known stations in Co. Cork (O'Mahony 1979). Sherkin is its most westerly locality in Europe.

It also occurs in an area of some three square miles at Tralee Bay, Co. Kerry (Scully 1919) and there is an old record from the Aran Islands. It has been overlooked in Ireland in recent years, although JRA and C.D. Preston rediscovered many of its 19th and early 20th century stations on coasts from north Co. Dublin to Carnsore Point, Co. Wexford (Akeroyd 1983).

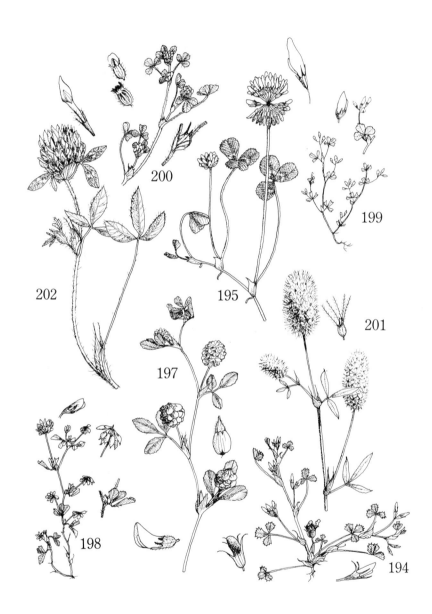

Clovers:

195 White Clover 198 Lesser Trefoil 200 Soft Clover 202 Red Clover

197 Hop Trefoil   199 Slender Trefoil 201 Hare's-foot Clover

201. *Trifolium arvense* L.   **Hare's-foot Clover, Cos mhaideach**

Rare on walls or rocky coastal heathland.

Sherkin (several stations around Abbey and Horseshoe Harbour, confirming records of Allin 1883, RAP 1900 and Polunin 1949; just east of Trabawn, BJL 1990; walls of Abbey nearest to strand)!, Cape Clear (road above west side of South Harbour)!

This species was recorded by Polunin (1949) on cliffs at Abbey Strand; it survives on one wall of the Abbey itself, mostly out of reach of visitors. It is currently diminished there by the restoration of the ruins, with the tidying up of the walls. The small population on Cape Clear is even more vulnerable and is threatened by the building of new houses. However, the plant is under no immediate threat at Horseshoe Harbour.

A very scattered plant in Ireland, mostly along eastern and south-eastern coasts but with just a few records from the west (for example, Gorumna Island in Connemara, McGough 1988).

202. *Trifolium pratense* L.   **Red Clover, Seamair dhearg**

Abundant in grassland and road-verges.

Sherkin!, Cape Clear!, Calfs!, Carthys!, Goat!, Long!, Castle!, Horse!, Skeams!, Heir!, Catalogues!, Sandy!, Quarantine!, Jeremy!, Spanish!, Inishleigh!, Mannin!

The native plant is variable but mostly decumbent to weakly ascending, with reddish or purplish-pink flowers, and is characteristic of maritime grasslands and unimproved, species-rich pastures. Fodder Red Clover (var. *sativum* Sturm) has been sown in improved pastures and is naturalised on road verges and in fields locally on Sherkin, Cape Clear and Heir. This variant may be recognised by its tall, more or less erect habit and larger heads of pale pink flowers.

203. *Lotus corniculatus* L.   **Common Bird's-foot Trefoil, Crobh éin**

Common in grassland, and rocky ground by the sea.

Sherkin!, Cape Clear!, Calfs!, Carthys!, Goat!, Long!, Castle!, Horse!, Skeams!, Heir!, Catalogues!, Sandy!, Quarantine!, Jeremy!, Spanish!, Inishleigh!, Mannin!

204. *Lotus uliginosus* Schkuhr   **Marsh Bird's-foot Trefoil, Crobh éin corraigh**

Bogs, damp fields and heaths, and road-verges.

Sherkin!, Cape Clear!, Calfs!, Carthys!, Goat!, Long!, Castle!, Horse!, Skeams!, Heir!, Catalogues!, Sandy!, Quarantine!, Spanish!, Inishleigh!, Mannin!

Readily distinguished from Common Bird's-foot Trefoil by the calyx-teeth, which spread conspicously in bud, and by the hollow stems.

205. *Lotus subbiflorus* Lag. (*L. hispidus* auct.)

Hairy Bird's-foot Trefoil, Crobh éin mosach

Rocky ground in heathland on south-facing slopes near the sea. **Irish Red Data Book - Rare.**

Sherkin (Foardree, KC 1992, JRA 1994; Horseshoe Harbour)!, Cape Clear (South Harbour; also sparingly near Lough Errul and just to west of East Pier, JRA 1994)!

A more delicate and finely hairy plant than the other two bird's-foot trefoils. This plant was first reported in Ireland on Cape Clear by J. Emmett O'Donovan, Mrs Bridges and others in May 1953 (O'Donovan 1953). It was discovered on Sherkin in 1974 (Conroy & Monaghan

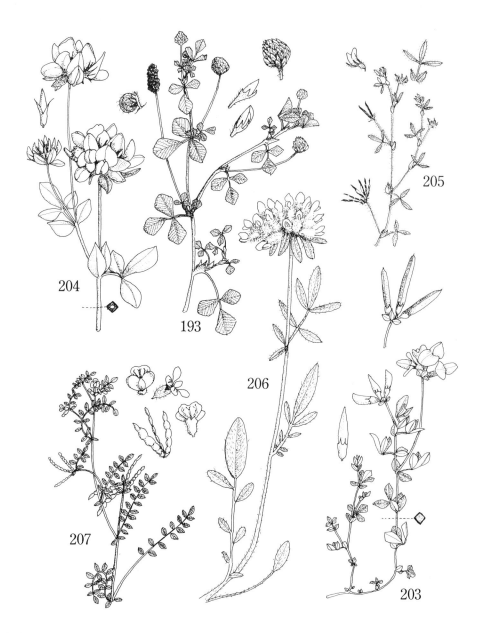

Bird's-foot Trefoils and relatives:

193 Black Medick

203 Common Bird's-foot Trefoil

204 Marsh Bird's-foot Trefoil

205 Hairy Bird's-foot Trefoil

206 Kidney-vetch

207 Bird's-foot

1975). The population at South Harbour is much the largest, but the plant's survival in (at least) four other stations is reassuring.

It is also known from the nearby mainland at Crookhaven, where it was observed by H. Hudson and J.E. O'Donovan in 1960 and 1965 (Hudson 1975), and Rock Island (O'Mahony 1994). It occurs in Ireland only at Roaringwater Bay and on the Co. Wexford coast (FitzGerald 1993).

206. *Anthyllis vulneraria* **L. (incl.** *A. dillenii* **auct. brit. et hibern.,** *A. vulneraria* **var.** *coccinea* **auct., non L.)**

Kidney-vetch, Méara Muire

Abundant in coastal grassland and on rocky ground and walls near the sea.

Sherkin!, Cape Clear!, Calfs!, Carthys!, Goat!, Little Goat!, Long!, Castle!, Horse!, Skeams!, Heir!, Catalogues!, Sandy! Quarantine!, Jeremy!, Spanish!, Inishleigh!, Mannin!

The distinctive variant of Kidney Vetch from Sherkin and other islands and coasts of Roaringwater Bay is close to *A. vulneraria* subsp. *lapponica* (N. Hyl.) Jalas, widespread in Scandinavia and Scotland. The stems are 10-30 cm, decumbent to ascending or rarely erect, the leaves inequifoliate, the calyx usually red-tipped, rather hairy; the corolla is cerise-pink, cream or sometimes pale (rarely bright) yellow. Some plants on Heir have almost crimson flowers, whilst those of plants on Cape Clear are mostly pale yellow.

Subsp. *lapponica* is apparently widespread in Ireland, at least in the north and west, where it was first reported by Cullen (1976). It is the common subspecies on the coast of Connemara; for example, collections from fixed dunes at Gowlaun (*J.R. Akeroyd H175, 28.6.1980*, **TCD**), a wall-top at Ardbear Bay (*J.R. Akeroyd H188, 30.6.1980*, **TCD**) and coastal grassland at the Coral Strand, Ballyconneely (*J.R. Akeroyd H191, 2.7.1980*, **TCD**). All plants recorded in Connemara have bright yellow flowers.

The pink-flowered plants from the islands of Roaringwater Bay, Ringarogy Island (JRA & DAW 1987) and adjacent coasts of Co. Cork and Co. Kerry (cf. Power 1845 - "var. *dillenii*. Red Kidneyvetch", Allin 1883, Scully 1916, p.70) probably deserve varietal rank. Further studies of these and other coastal plants in Ireland and Britain are in progress (J.R. Akeroyd & P.D. Sell, unpublished data).

207. *Ornithopus perpusillus* **L.**   Bird's-foot, Crúba éin

Locally common on shallow soils over rock outcrops in coastal grassland. **Irish Red Data Book - Rare.**

Sherkin (E. end)!, Cape Clear!, Long!, Horse!, Skeam W!

Polunin found a few plants on cliffs above Abbey Strand, where it has been refound several times by Mrs Bridges (in 1953, and on Cape Clear) and others (Fahy 1975). Fahy reported it growing with Hairy Bird's-foot Trefoil, the second record of that species from Sherkin. Bird's-foot has several stations on Sherkin, in the area bounded by the eastern side of Kinish Harbour, Abbey Strand and Horseshoe Harbour, and is locally common elsewhere. The species has a scattered distribution in south & east-central Ireland, mostly near the coast, and has probably been overlooked. Its Irish headquarters are Roaringwater Bay and parts of Co. Wexford (J.R. Akeroyd & R. FitzGerald unpublished).

Recorded from "rocky ground by the sea at Goleen" by Phillips (RAP 1896, 1901) and at three stations on Rock Island opposite Crookhaven in 1992 (T. O'Mahony pers. comm. 1993).

OXALIDACEAE - wood sorrels

*208. *Oxalis articulata* **Savigny**   Pink-sorrel, Seamsóg ghlúineach

Cultivated for ornament and sometimes naturalised near gardens.

Sherkin (mostly around Murphy's Bar)!, Cape Clear!, Horse!, Heir!

209. *Oxalis acetosella* L.   Wood-sorrel, Seamsóg

Sheltered places, usually in the shade of bracken.

Sherkin!, Cape Clear!, Spanish!, Mannin!

GERANIACEAE – cranesbills and storksbills

The wild cranesbills or geraniums are plants of grassland and open places. Garden 'Geraniums' are mostly species or cultivars of *Pelargonium*, introduced from South Africa.

*210. *Geranium pyrenaicum* Burm. fil.   Hedgerow Cranesbill, Crobh na bhfál

Grassy place, probably introduced with cattle fodder.

W Calf (PCH & MWR 1994, confirming records of Polunin 1950, PW 1975 and RF 1993)!

211. *Geranium molle* L.   Dove's-foot Cranesbill, Crobh bog

Frequent in open ground and short grassland; sometimes on upper part of shingle strands.

Sherkin!, Cape Clear!, M & E Calf!, Carthys!, Long!, Castle!, Horse!, Skeams!, Heir!, Catalogues!, Spanish!

The commonest cranesbill and variable in habit; white-flowered plants occur on Horse. Robust plants from Horse with larger flowers superficially resemble Hedgerow Cranesbill. Records of Small-flowered Cranesbill (*G. pusillum* L.) and Round-leaved Cranesbill (*G. rotundifolium* L.) from the islands probably refer to this species.

212. *Geranium dissectum* L.   Cut-leaved Cranesbill, Crobh giobach

Common in grassland and on dry waysides.

Sherkin!, Cape Clear!, Calfs!, Carthys!, Long!, Castle!, Horse!, Skeam W (LCW 1982), Skeam E!, Heir!, Spanish!

213. *Geranium robertianum* L.   Herb Robert, Ruithéal rí

Common on road-verges and walls; sometimes on shingle strands.

Sherkin!, Cape Clear!, Long!, Castle!, Horse!, Skeam E!, Heir!, Spanish!

The plants on Castle apparently belong to subsp. *maritimum* (Bab.) H.G. Baker, a variable and rather ill-defined, dwarf coastal variant of this species, characteristic of shingle strands.

214. *Geranium purpureum* Vill.   Little Robin, Eireaball rí

Rare on walls and shingle strands. **Irish Red Data Book - Vulnerable.**

Long (NR 1993; still present, also at two other stations, JRA, PCH & MWR 1994)!

The only other Irish stations for this plant are in and around Cork City, where it survives precariously at several sites, mostly on old walls (O'Mahony 1985). It has not been seen recently at its other station in Dungarvan, Co. Waterford (Curtis & McGough 1988). The plants on Long therefore represent a significant extension of the known range of the species in Ireland. It is possibly not native in Ireland and the plants on Long, near to a landing place and with a number of weeds, suggest that it may be a long-term introduction. The main strand population especially is strong, with over 100 plants counted in 1993 and 1995.

It can be distinguished from Herb Robert by the smaller flowers, yellow rather than orange stamens, and more wrinkled fruits; many botanists regard these two plants as subspecies. Little Robin more usually occurs on lime-rich soils or crevices of limestone walls.

215. *Erodium maritimum* **(L.) L'Her.**   **Sea Storksbill, Creagach mara**

Locally common on wall-tops and bare ground near the sea, mostly on Cape Clear.

Sherkin (RAP; by harbour, JRA 1987), Cape Clear!

A characteristic member of the flora of Cape Clear, on walls and roadsides near North and South Harbours, including a strong population outside the youth hostel. It also occurs on sandy ground around rabbit burrows at the west end of Lough Errul. There is an old mainland record from Crookhaven (Allin 1883), and it was described as "frequent in the Schull promontory" (RAP). This species is almost absent from Kerry (Scully 1916).

The flowers usually lack petals.

216. *Erodium cicutarium* **(L.) L'Her.**   **Common Storksbill, Creagach**

Sherkin (Polunin 1949), Spanish (LCW 1982).

An unconfirmed record of this plant from Cape Clear may refer to Musk Storksbill.

217. *Erodium moschatum* **(L.) L'Her.**   **Musk Storksbill, Creagach muscach**

Locally common on wall-tops, roadsides, rock outcrops and bare ground near the sea; also around buildings.

Sherkin!, Cape Clear!, M Calf (PW 1975), E Calf (MQ 1975), Long!, Castle (PCH & MWR 1994)!, Heir!

Allin (1883) stated "Inisherkin Island, chiefly near the sea - frequent", although Polunin (1949) recorded one station only, near farm buildings at the western end of Sherkin - where it still grows. Its main habitat is wall-tops, where it cohabits on Cape Clear with Sea Storksbill, including the wall outside the Youth Hostel. On the mainland it grows on walls in Baltimore.

Musk Storksbill is variable in habit, generally prostrate and diminutive, but it can form a robust, erect plant up to 30 cm tall where it has shelter and a richer soil. The petals fall after midday, making it inconspicuous.

Thought by some to be a declining species in Ireland, this attractive plant has been found or rediscovered in many places in recent years, especially in the east. Scully (1916) gives a number of records from Kerry, especially around Dingle, where it flourished until at least the late 1970s (for example, *J.R. Akeroyd H79, 15.6.79*, **TCD**).

LINACEAE - flaxes

218. *Linum bienne* **Miller**   **Pale Flax, Líon beag**

Rare on banks by the sea.

Sherkin (confirming record of Polunin 1949)!, Heir!

Scarce in western Ireland.

219. *Linum catharticum* **L.**   **Purging Flax, Lus na mban sí**

Short coastal grassland.

Sherkin!, Cape Clear!, M & E Calf!, Long!, Horse!, Skeams!, Heir!, Catalogues!, Sandy!, Spanish!

A compact, bushy plant on a shingle strand on Long (BM & MWR 1995) is probably forma *dunense* Fries, reported from a few places in Britain but not before apparently from Ireland.

220. *Radiola linoides* Roth   Allseed, Gathán lín

Bare peaty ground.

Sherkin!, Cape Clear!, M & E Calf!, Long!, Castle!, Horse!, Heir!, Spanish!

Recorded from Schull (Allin 1883) and from Ringarogy Island (JRA & DAW 1987).

EUPHORBIACEAE – spurges

The white sap that exudes from the cut stems of these plants was a traditional island cure for warts (O'Reilly 1994). Annual Mercury (*Mercurialis annua* L.), related to the spurges, was reported as "Plentiful nr Baltimore 1898" (RAP).

221. *Euphorbia hyberna* L.   Irish Spurge, Bainne caoin

Locally common, mostly on larger islands, in sheltered places along lanes, in heathland and on sea-cliffs.

Sherkin!, Cape Clear!, E Calf (PW 1975, PSWJ 1979), Goat!, Long!, Castle!, Skeam E!, Heir!, Spanish!, Inishleigh!

222. *Euphorbia helioscopia* L.   Sun Spurge, Lus na bhfaithní

Frequent on cultivated ground; sometimes on strands.

Sherkin!, Cape Clear!, W & E Calf!, Long!, Horse!, Skeams!, Heir!

223. *Euphorbia peplus* L.   Petty Spurge, Gearr nimhe

Local on cultivated and waste ground, also sand and shingle strands.

Sherkin!, Cape Clear!, Long!, Skeam E!, Heir!

A weed of flower beds and tubs in Baltimore that is surprisingly scarce in the islands.

224. *Euphorbia portlandica* L.   Portland Spurge, Spuirse ghainimh

Upper part of strands.

Sherkin!, Long!, Skeam E (PCH & MWR 1994)!

225. *Euphorbia paralias* L.   Sea Spurge, Bainne léana

Strands and sand-dunes.

Sherkin!, Cape Clear!, M Calf (MQ 1975, LCW 1982, T O'M 1992)!, Long!

POLYGALACEAE - milkworts

226. *Polygala vulgaris* **L.**   **Common Milkwort, Lus an bhainne**

Short coastal grassland.

Sherkin!, Cape Clear!, Calfs!, Long!, Horse!, Skeam W (LCW 1982), Heir!, Quarantine!

Almost always with blue flowers in the islands, but a white-flowered variant occurs on Horse (BM & MWR 1995).

227. *Polygala serpyllifolia* **J.A.C. Hose**   **Heath Milkwort, Na deirfiúiríní**

Grassy heaths.

Sherkin!, Cape Clear!, Calfs!, Goat!, Long!, Castle!, Horse!, Skeams!, Heir!, Catalogues!, Sandy!, Spanish!, Inishleigh!, Mannin!

ACERACEAE - maples

*228. *Acer pseudoplatanus* **L.**   **Sycamore, Seiceamóir**

Widely planted for shelter and self-seeding.

Sherkin!, Cape Clear!, Long!, Castle!, Horse (recently planted)!, Heir!, Spanish!

BALSAMINACEAE - balsams

*229. *Impatiens glandulifera* **Royle**   **Himalayan Balsam, Lus na pléisce**

Introduced for ornament; likely to escape.

Cape Clear (North Harbour, JRA & BM 1995)!

This invasive plant of river-banks and damp or shady places will probably spread - the seeds disperse explosively.

AQUIFOLIACEAE - hollies

230. *Ilex aquifolium* **L.**   **Holly, Cuileann**

Occasional in hedges and as an isolated tree.

Sherkin!, Castle!, Spanish!

CELASTRACEAE - spindles

*231. *Euonymus japonicus* **L. fil.**   **Japanese Spindle, Feoras Seapánach**

Planted for evergreen hedges and shelter.

Sherkin!, Cape Clear!, Horse!, Heir!

232. *Euonymus europaeus* **L.**   **Spindle, Feoras**

Hedges and in sheltered gullies cutting into low sea-cliffs.

Cape Clear (KC 1992, confirming record of Edmunds 1960)!, Horse (S.E. end)!

It also grows at the head of the inlet by the quay at Turk Head.

MALVACEAE - mallows

233. *Malva sylvestris* **L.**   **Common Mallow, Lus na meall Muire**

Rather rare on waysides and strands.

Sherkin!, Cape Clear!, E Calf (BM 1995, confirming record of *O. Polunin 119*, 8.1948, **BM** and PSWJ 1979)!, Long (LCW 1982), Horse!, Skeam W!

Also by the Castle at Baltimore. This plant is often associated with human habitation. It has a long history of use as a potherb and medicinal plant.

    A record of Dwarf Mallow (*M. neglecta* Wallr.) from Sherkin was apparently a misidentification of Common Mallow. Allin (1883) recorded Small Mallow (*M. pusilla* Sm.), as *M. rotundifolia* L., from Toe Head and near Skibbereen. Musk Mallow (*M. moschata* L.) was once recorded on Sherkin (MB 1964), perhaps as a garden escape.

234. *Lavatera arborea* **L.**   **Tree Mallow, Hocas ard**

Local on strands and sea-cliffs, where it may be native; also around houses as an obvious escape from cultivation.

Sherkin!, Cape Clear!, Long!, Horse!, Skeam W!, Heir!

235. *Althaea officinalis* **L.**   **Marsh Mallow, Leamhach**

Local on damp ground, often near houses or ruins, sometimes forming "large clumps" as noted by O'Donovan & O'Regan (1952).

Sherkin (Polunin 1949; S. side of Kinish Harbour, JRA & SLJ 1986, JRA & DAW 1987; W. side of Kinish Harbour, RF 1993)!, Cape Clear!

Long known in the islands; recorded by J. Drummond in 1820 on Cape Clear and still there in 1896 (Colgan & Scully 1898). Allin (1883) and Phillips (RAP 1896) reported this species from Sherkin and Baltimore. The plants at Rugher Strand had disappeared by 1990, covered by a pile of grit used for road improvements, but R. FitzGerald's record happily reconfirms this attractive and interesting member of Sherkin's flora.

    It is probably a relic of former medicinal use, for example in cough mixtures, as in Co. Donegal (Hart 1898).

ELAEAGNACEAE - sea-buckthorns and elaeagnus

*236. Hippophae rhamnoides L.   **Sea-buckthorn, Draighean mara**

Planted to bind an eroding sand-dune.

Sherkin (Cow Strand)!

First recorded in 1992 (JRA & KC); also recently planted for ornament at North Harbour, Cape Clear. Native on sand-dunes in eastern Britain.

HYPERICACEAE - St John's-worts

237. *Hypericum androsaemum* **L.**   **Tutsan, Meas torc allta**

Shady, sheltered places on the larger islands.

Sherkin!, Cape Clear!, Horse!, Heir!, Spanish!

238. *Hypericum pulchrum* **L.**   **Slender St John's-wort, Beathnua baineann**

Dry heaths and banks.

Sherkin!, Cape Clear!, E Calf!, Long!, Horse!, Skeams!, Heir!, Catalogues!, Sandy!, Jeremy!, Spanish!, Inishleigh!, Mannin!

239. *Hypericum elodes* **L.**   **Marsh St John's-wort, Luibh an chiorraithe**

Margins of loughs and peaty pools, often forming a distinct band.

Sherkin!, Cape Clear!, Long!, Heir!, Sandy (LCW 1982), Spanish!, Mannin (LCW 1982).

240. *Hypericum humifusum* **L.**   **Trailing St John's-wort, Beathnua sraoilleach**

Banks and rock outcrops.

Sherkin!, Cape Clear!, E Calf (LCW 1982), Long!, Castle!, Horse!, Skeams!, Heir!, Spanish!, Inishleigh!, Mannin (LCW 1982).

241. *Hypericum tetrapterum* **Fries   Square-stalked St John's-wort, Beathnua fireann**

Waysides and damp ground.

Sherkin!, Cape Clear!, M & E Calf!, Castle!, Horse!, Heir!, Sandy!, Spanish!

242. *Hypericum maculatum Crantz*   **Imperforate St John's-wort, Beathnua gan smál**

M Calf (PCH & MWR 1994)!

All Irish plants of this variable species apparently belong to subsp. *obtusiusculum* (Tourlet) Hayek (Scannell & Synnott 1987).

VIOLACEAE – pansies and violets

The perennial wild violets and the annual (or short-lived perennial) pansies are smaller and more delicate than their garden counterparts. The flowers are also unscented. Large-flowered pansies are commonly grown in gardens in the islands.

*243. *Viola odorata* **L.**   **Sweet Violet, Sailchuach chumhra**

Garden escape; this popular plant is probably not native in Western Ireland.

Cape Clear (Edmunds 1960).

244. *Viola riviniana* **Reichenb.**   **Common Dog-violet, Fanaigse**

Heaths, dry banks and grassy walls.

Sherkin!, Cape Clear!, Calfs!, Goat!, Long!, Castle!, Horse!, Skeams!, Heir!, Catalogues!, Sandy!, Jeremy!, Spanish!, Inishleigh!, Mannin!

Plants near the sea, especially on the exposed heathland of Cape Clear itself, are short and compact, with smaller leaves. They can be referred to var. *minor* (Gregory) Valentine.

245. *Viola canina* L.   Heath Dog-violet, Sailchuach mhóna

Rare, but perhaps overlooked, in heathland by the sea.

Sherkin (near Marine Station, PCH & MWR 1994)!, Heir (W. end, JRA, PCH & MWR 1994)!

246. *Viola lactea* Sm.   Pale Dog-violet, Sailchuach liath

Rare in heathland. **Irish Red Data Book - Vulnerable.**

Sherkin (Foardree; Horseshoe Harbour; Kinish Harbour, KC 1992; near Marine Station, NR 1993)!, Cape Clear (Edmunds 1960).

There are two other extant stations in West Cork of this rare violet, which has its Irish headquarters in Co. Cork and Kerry. Sherkin is one of its most important Irish stations. Putative hybrids with Common Dog-violet have been observed on the mainland at Three Castles Head (O'Mahony 1993) and may well occur on Sherkin.

247. *Viola palustris* L.   Marsh Violet, Sailchuach chorraigh

Marshy and boggy ground; the leaves are much more conspicuous than the flowers.

Sherkin!, Cape Clear!, Spanish!, Mannin!

248. *Viola tricolor* L. subsp. *curtisii* (E. Forster) Syme

Dune Pansy, Goirmín duimhche

Sandy grassland and open, sandy ground by the sea.

Sherkin (Tragowenmore Bay [Cow Strand], Polunin 1949), E Calf!, Horse (RF 1993).

Polymorphic in flower colour (yellow/blue). The flowers of the plants on Sherkin (Polunin specimens, **BM**) and East Calf are mostly yellow.

249. *Viola arvensis* Murray (*V. obtusifolia* Jordan)   Field Pansy, Lus croí

Occasional on cultivated and disturbed ground.

Sherkin (MWR 1995, confirming record of Polunin 1949)!, Cape Clear!, Horse!, Heir!

CISTACEAE - rockroses and sunroses

250. *Tuberaria guttata* (L.) Fourr.   Spotted Rockrose, Grianrós breac

Rare, but often many individual plants present, on rock outcrops in exposed heathland near the sea. The classic rarity of Roaringwater Bay. **Irish Red Data Book - Rare.**

E Calf (KC 1992)!, Long (JRA, PCH & MWR 1994)!, Heir (JRA & NR 1993; second station, MWR 1994)!

These records confirm old reports, based on Phillips' work, of the species from East Calf and Heir, where it was not relocated by Polunin (1950). The station on Long fills a gap in the West Cork distribution of this Mediterranean plant, so rare in Ireland and north-western Europe.

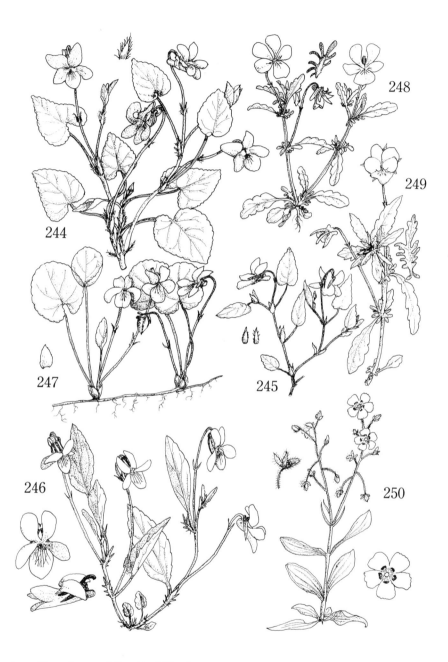

Violets, Pansies and Spotted Rockrose:

244 Common Dog-violet   246 Pale Dog-violet   248 Dune Pansy   250 Spotted Rockrose

245 Heath Dog-violet   247 Marsh Violet   249 Field Pansy

89

The other Irish stations are all on islands or peninsulas in the extreme west, on the coasts of West Mayo and Connemara, just to the north of Roaringwater Bay on Sheep's Head and in several places around Three Castles Head and Crookhaven, West Cork (O'Mahony 1993, 1994). Recent monitoring has shown that Spotted Rockrose survives well in West Galway, on Gorumna Island (McGough 1988) and Inishbofin (Brodie & Sheehy Skeffington 1990).

There is a curious J. Drummond record from Cape Clear (Power 1845) of *Helianthemum vulgare* Gaertner [*H. nummularium* (L.) Miller], which might refer to Spotted Rockrose. The plant could well have been overlooked at other sites, flowering as it does in early summer and the flimsy petals often fallen by afternoon.

The Roaringwater Bay plants are mostly small in stature, with many bracts amongst the flowers. Such plants, similar to those from Wales and Three Castles Head, have been called subsp. *breweri* (Planchon) E. Warb., but the variation between these and plants from the continent is continuous (Proctor 1962).

TAMARICACEAE - tamarisks

*251. *Tamarix gallica* **L. (*T. anglica* auct.)**   **Tamarisc, Tamaraisc**

Occasionally planted for shelter and ornament; salt-tolerant.

Cape Clear!

ELATINACEAE - waterworts

252. *Elatine hexandra* **(Lapierre) DC.**   **Six-stamened Waterwort, Bosán na díge**

Sherkin (extreme W. end of island, Polunin 1949).

LYTHRACEAE - water purslanes

253. *Lythrum salicaria* **L.**   **Purple Loosestrife, Créachtach**

Common in marshes and ditches and along hedges and road-verges. One of the most attractive flowers of late summer, colouring the landscape in some places.

Sherkin!, Cape Clear!, W & E Calf!, Long!, Castle (LCW 1982), Horse!, Heir!, Catalogues!, Sandy!, Spanish!, Inishleigh!

254. *Lythrum portula* **(L.) D.A. Webb (*Peplis portula* L.)**

Water-purslane, Puirpín uisce

Local in open, wet ground, often by paths and in places trampled by cattle.

Sherkin!, Cape Clear!, M Calf!, Long!, Castle!, Spanish!

ONAGRACEAE - willowherbs

Willowherbs are mostly plants of disturbed or damp ground. Fuchsia is, however, the more familiar member of this mostly American family.

*255. *Fuchsia magellanica* **Lam.**   **Fuchsia, Fiúise**

Common as a hedge-plant on the larger islands, especially in gardens and near houses, and locally naturalised; a feature of the scenery of the islands and West Cork. It was originally introduced from Chile.

Sherkin!, Cape Clear!, Long!, Castle!, Horse!, Heir!, Spanish (LCW 1982).

256. *Circaea lutetiana* **L.**   **Enchanter's-nightshade, Fuinseagach**

Rare in shade amongst trees and scrub.

Spanish (PCH & MWR 1994)!

257. *Epilobium parviflorum* **Schreber**   **Hoary Willowherb, Saileachán liath**

Common on waysides and disturbed ground.

Sherkin!, Cape Clear!, E Calf!, Long!, Castle!, Horse!, Skeam E!, Heir!, Sandy!, Spanish!, Inishleigh!

258. *Epilobium montanum* **L.**   **Broad-leaved Willowherb, Saileachán leathan**

Common on waysides and disturbed ground.

Sherkin!, Cape Clear!, M Calf!, Long!, Castle!, Horse!, Skeam E!, Heir!, Spanish!

259. *Epilobium obscurum* **Schreber**   **Short-fruited Willowherb, Saileachán caol**

Common on waysides and disturbed ground.

Sherkin!, Cape Clear!, M & E Calf!, Long!, Horse!, Skeams!, Heir!, Catalogues!, Sandy!, Quarantine!, Inishleigh!, Mannin (LCW 1982).

Records of Square-stalked Willowherb (*E. tetragonum* L.) probably belong here.

260. *Epilobium palustre* **L.**   **Marsh Willowherb, Saileachán corraigh**

Widespread in wet places.

Sherkin!, Cape Clear!, M Calf!, E Calf (LCW 1982), Long!, Castle!, Horse!, Skeam E!, Heir!, Catalogues!, Spanish!, Inishleigh!

*261. *Epilobium brunnescens* **(Cockayne) Raven & Engelhorn**

                              New Zealand Willowherb, Saileachán sraoilleach

Damp ground and walls.

Sherkin (near The Cross, PCH & MWR 1994)!

Still local in Co. Cork, although abundant in parts of Kerry.

HALORAGACEAE - water-milfoils

262. *Myriophyllum spicatum* **L.**   **Spiked Water-milfoil, Líonánach**

Loughs and pools.

Sherkin (Lough Ordree, OP, unpublished notes), M & E Calf!

263. *Myriophyllum alterniflorum* **DC.**   **Alternate Water-milfoil, Líonán crom**

Peaty pools.

Sherkin (Polunin 1950, JRA 1992)!

HIPPURIDACEAE - mare's-tails

264. *Hippuris vulgaris* L.   **Mare's-tail, Colgrach**

Occasional in marshes.

Sherkin (Tramore, Trabawn)!

CORNACEAE - dogwoods

*265. *Griselinia littoralis* **Raoul**   **Griselinia, Grisilinia**

Planted for shelter, mainly in gardens; introduced from New Zealand.

Sherkin (near Post Office)!, Castle (BM & MWR 1995)!

ARALIACEAE - ivies

266. *Hedera helix* **L.**   **Ivy, Eidhneán**

Shady places, cliffs, walls, hedges and covering ruins.

Sherkin!, Cape Clear!, Calfs!, Long!, Castle!, Horse!, Skeams!, Heir!, Catalogues!, Sandy!, Spanish!, Inishleigh!, Mannin!

Ivy leaves were applied to corns (O'Reilly 1994).

UMBELLIFERAE – fennel, hemlock, parsley and related plants

The flowers in this family are massed in umbrella-shaped clusters. Many of these plants are familiar garden vegetables (e.g. carrots, parsnips and celery) or herbs (e.g. parsley, fennel and coriander). Several others are, however, poisonous.

267. *Hydrocotyle vulgaris* **L.**   **Marsh Pennywort, Lus na pingine**

Common in wet, grassy and boggy places.

Sherkin!, Cape Clear!, Calfs!, Goat!, Long!, Castle!, Horse!, Skeams!, Heir!, Catalogues!, Sandy!, Spanish!, Inishleigh!, Mannin!

268. *Eryngium maritimum* **L.**   **Sea-holly, Cuileann trá**

Scarce on sand or shingle strands and foredunes.

Sherkin (confirming record of Polunin 1949)!, M Calf!, Horse!, Heir!

[*269. *Eryngium campestre* **L.**   **Field Eryngo, Cuileann léana**

Sherkin; extinct.

Perhaps - for botanists at least - the most famous member of Sherkin's flora, reported by Phillips (1901), who was of the opinion that it was native. It had apparently disappeared by the time of Polunin's visits (Polunin 1950) and, despite a search, was not found by O'Donovan & O'Regan (1952). It may be native in a few places in southern England, but probably came to Sherkin with imported fodder.]

270. *Smyrnium olusatrum* L.   Alexanders, Lusrán grándubh

Rare by roads, walls and houses; a relic of culinary use. Also found by the Castle at Baltimore.

Sherkin (by Abbey and near Castle)!

The yellow flowers and large, dark green, shiny leaves are distinctive in spring and early summer.

271. *Conopodium majus* (Gouan) Loret & Barrandon   Earth-nut, Cúlarán

Local in heathland and pastures; often beneath bracken.

Sherkin!, Cape Clear!, Long!, Castle (LCW 1982), Horse!, Skeam W!, Heir!, Spanish!, Mannin!

272. *Berula erecta* (Hudson) Coville   Lesser Water-parsnip, Ráib uisce

Wet places.

Sherkin!, Cape Clear!, W & M Calfs!, Long!, Horse!, Heir!

273. *Crithmum maritimum* L.   Rock Samphire, Craobhraic

Locally frequent on seaside rocks and cliffs, rarely amongst grass by the sea.

Sherkin!, Cape Clear!, Badger!, Calfs!, Carthys!, Goat!, Long!, Castle!, Horse!, Skeams!, Heir!, Catalogues!, Spanish!, Inishleigh!, Mannin!

274. *Oenanthe lachenalii* C.C. Gmelin   Parsley Water-dropwort, Dathabha peirsile

Brackish marshes by the sea.

Sherkin!, Cape Clear (LCW 1982), Heir!, Sandy!, Spanish!, Mannin!

275. *Oenanthe crocata* L.   Hemlock Water-dropwort, Dathabha bán

Frequent in marshes and wet fields. A very poisonous plant.

Sherkin!, Cape Clear!, E Calf!, Long!, Castle!, Heir!, Sandy!, Quarantine!, Spanish!, Inishleigh!, Mannin!

*276. *Foeniculum vulgare* Miller   Fennel, Finéal

Rare as a garden relic or escape.

Sherkin!, Cape Clear!, Long!, Heir!

Also on roadsides near Baltimore (O'Donovan & O'Regan 1952, JRA & DAW 1987). Its native status in Co. Cork and elsewhere is debatable, but note the comment of Allin (1883): "May be found along our coasts in abundance, and apparently indigenous".

277. *Conium maculatum* L.   Hemlock, Moing mhear

Local on waste ground, especially around ruins.

Sherkin (around Castle and nearby houses)!, Cape Clear!, Long!, Horse!, Skeam W!, Heir!

A very poisonous, carrot-like plant, recognisable by its feathery leaves and purple-blotched stems; probably a relic of former medicinal use.

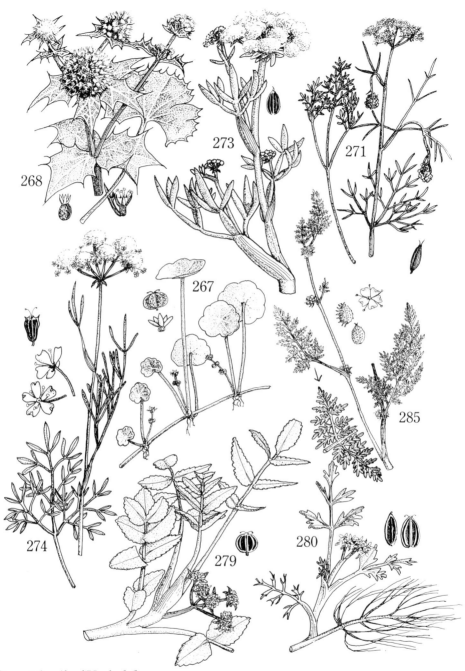

Carrot family ('Umbels'):

267 Marsh Pennywort

268 Sea-holly

271 Earth-nut

273 Rock Samphire

274 Parsley Water-dropwort

279 Fool's Water-cress

280 Lesser Marshwort

285 Knotted Hedge-parsley

278. *Apium graveolens* **L.**   **Wild Celery, Smaileog**

Brackish marshes near the sea.

Heir (S.E. end, BM & MWR 1995)!

A rare plant of Irish coasts, with very few records from Co. Cork.

279. *Apium nodiflorum* **(L.). Lag.**   **Fool's Water-cress, Gunna uisce**

Streams, marshes and roadside runnels.

Sherkin!, Cape Clear!, Calfs!, Long!, Castle!, Horse!, Skeam E!, Heir!, Sandy!

280. *Apium inundatum* **(L.) Reichenb. fil.**   **Lesser Marshwort, Smaileog bháite**

Pools near the sea; growing more or less submerged.

Sherkin (Trabawn, Sherkin Point)!, Cape Clear (confirming record of Sharrock 1965)!, M
Calf!, Long!

*281. *Petroselinum crispum* **(Miller) A.W. Hill**   **Garden Parsley, Peirsil gharraí**

Old walls and disturbed ground, as a relic of cultivation.

Sherkin (Castle)!, Skeam W (JRA & NR 1993)!

Known at the Castle on Sherkin for a century at least (RAP 1896, Polunin 1949). Polunin
(1949) also found this plant at the Abbey. It is often associated with ancient castles and church
buildings in Ireland (see records in Colgan & Scully 1898). These naturalised plants have
uncrisped leaves.

282. *Angelica sylvestris* **L.**   **Wild Angelica, Gallfheabhrán**

Damp places, ditches and tall grassland near the sea.

Sherkin!, Cape Clear!, Long!, Castle!, Horse!, Heir!, Sandy!, Quarantine!, Spanish!, Inishleigh
(LCW 1982).

*283. *Pastinaca sativa* **L.**   **Parsnip, Cuirdín bán**

Open ground; perhaps a relic of cultivation.

Sherkin (O'Connor's Field, LCW 1982).

284. *Heracleum sphondylium* **L.**   **Hogweed, Feabhrán**

Waysides and tall grassland.

Sherkin!, Cape Clear!, Calfs!, Carthys!, Goat!, Little Goat!, Long!, Castle!, Horse!, Skeams!,
Heir!, Catalogues!, Sandy!, Quarantine!, Spanish!, Inishleigh!

285. *Torilis nodosa* **(L.) Gaertner**   **Knotted Hedge-parsley, Lus na gcloch fuail**

Very rare in rocky coastal grassland, disturbed ground or road-verges, near houses or ruins.

Sherkin (Allin 1883, Polunin 1949), Horse (E. end; PW 1975, JRA 1992, PCH & MWR 1994)!,
Skeam W!, Heir (causeway, JRA 1994)!

Reported from both "Inisherkin Island" and Toe Head to the east of Baltimore by Allin (1883),
and from Bro[w] Head and Baltimore (RAP 1896). A scarce plant in Ireland.

286. *Torilis japonica* (Houtt.) DC.　　　　**Upright Hedge-parsley, Fionnas fáil**

Common in lanes and by hedges.

Sherkin!, Cape Clear!, E Calf (PW 1975), Long!, Horse!, Heir!, Spanish!

287. *Daucus carota* **L. subsp.** *gummifer* **Hooker fil.**　　**Wild Carrot, Mealbhacán mara**

Coastal grassland, lanesides and grassy walls.

Sherkin!, Cape Clear!, Calfs!, Long!, Castle!, Horse!, Skeams!, Heir!, Catalogues!, Sandy!, Spanish!

ERICACEAE - heathers and heaths

Heather, heaths and their relatives are dwarf shrubs of usually lime-poor soils that form a major element of the vegetation of West Cork.

288. *Erica tetralix* **L.**　　　　　　**Cross-leaved Heath, Fraoch naoscaí**

Damp heaths and hummocks in bogs.

Sherkin!, Cape Clear!, Calfs!, Goat!, Long!, Castle!, Horse!, Skeams!, Heir!, Catalogues!, Sandy!, Jeremy!, Spanish!, Inishleigh!, Mannin!

289. *Erica cinerea* **L.**　　　　　　**Bell Heather, Fraoch cloigíneach**

Common in heathland; this plant colours the landscape in late summer.

Sherkin!, Cape Clear!, Calfs!, Goat!, Long!, Castle!, Horse!, Skeams!, Heir!, Catalogues!, Sandy!, Quarantine!, Jeremy!, Spanish!, Inishleigh!, Mannin!

A white-flowered variant occurs on Cape Clear.

290. *Calluna vulgaris* **(L.) Hull**　　　　**Heather or Ling, Fraoch mór**

Dominant dwarf shrub of heathland.

Sherkin!, Cape Clear!, Calfs!, Goat!, Long!, Castle!, Horse!, Skeams!, Heir!, Catalogues!, Sandy!, Quarantine!, Jeremy!, Spanish!, Inishleigh!, Mannin!

A white-flowered variant occurs on Sherkin.

291. *Vaccinium myrtillus* **L.**　　　　　　**Bilberry, Fraochán**

Rare on rocky hilltops.

Cape Clear (Edmunds 1960).

PRIMULACEAE – primrose and pimpernels

292. *Primula vulgaris* **Hudson**　　　　　　**Primrose, Sabhaircín**

Common on grassy banks, fields and road-verges.

Sherkin!, Cape Clear!, M & E Calf!, Goat!, Long!, Castle!, Horse!, Skeams!, Heir!, Catalogues!, Sandy!, Spanish!, Mannin!

Cowslip (*P. veris* L.) has been reported from Sherkin and other islands, apparently in error. The comments of O'Donovan & O'Regan (1952) about this species are interesting: "Was common and widespread in West Cork sixty years ago. Now is extremely rare. Probably the modern system of farming, with extensive tillaging and very little permanent pasture, is to blame."

293. *Lysimachia vulgaris* L.   **Yellow Loosestrife, Breallán léana**

Damp places.

Sherkin (NR 1993)!

*294. *Lysimachia nummularia* L.   **Creeping Jenny, Lus an dá phingin**

Damp, shady ground near ruins; probably introduced.

Spanish (NR 1993)!

295. *Lysimachia nemorum* L.   **Yellow Pimpernel, Lus Cholm Cille**

Damp ground

Sherkin!, Cape Clear (Polunin, unpublished notes; Sharrock 1965), E Calf!, Spanish!, Mannin!

296. *Glaux maritima* L.   **Sea Milkwort, Lus an tsaillte**

Common on sand and shingle strands, salt-marshes and coastal rocks.

Sherkin!, Cape Clear!, Calfs!, Carthys!, Long!, Castle!, Horse!, Skeams!, Heir!, Catalogues!, Sandy!, Quarantine!, Jeremy!, Spanish!, Inishleigh!, Mannin!

297. *Anagallis minima* (L.) E.H.L. Krause   **Chaffweed, Falcaire beag**

Damp, open ground, usually flooded in winter.

Sherkin (Polunin 1949; Horseshoe Harbour, JRA 1992)!, Cape Clear!, Long!

298. *Anagallis tenella* (L.) L.   **Bog Pimpernel, Falcaire corraigh**

Frequent in boggy places, wet meadows and damp areas in coastal heath; sometimes on grassy walls.

Sherkin!, Cape Clear!, Calfs!, Long!, Castle!, Horse!, Skeams!, Heir!, Catalogues!, Sandy!, Spanish!

299. *Anagallis arvensis* L.   **Scarlet Pimpernel, Falcaire fiáin**

Open, often damp ground, waysides and cultivated land.

Sherkin!, Cape Clear!, Calfs!, Long!, Castle!, Horse!, Skeams!, Heir!, Catalogues!, Sandy!, Spanish!, Inishleigh!

The usual plant in native habitats is var. *carnea* Schrank, with flesh-coloured petals. The plants on disturbed or cultivated ground have scarlet petals (var. *arvensis*). Plants with flesh-coloured flowers are common on the coasts of Ireland (*fide* JRA), and the odd published comment suggests that they are widespread in the west of Britain and the Channel Islands (Allen 1950).

300. *Samolus valerandi* L.   **Brookweed, Falcaire uisce**

Frequent in wet places and rocks near the sea.

Sherkin!, Cape Clear!, Calfs!, Long!, Castle!, Skeam E!, Heir!, Catalogues!, Sandy!, Spanish!

PLUMBAGINACEAE - thrifts and sea-lavenders

301. *Armeria maritima* **(Miller) Willd.**   **Thrift, Rabhán**

Abundant on coastal rocks and cliffs; also saltmarshes and coastal heaths.

Sherkin!, Cape Clear!, Bird!, Badger!, Calfs!, Carthys!, Goat!, Little Goat!, Long!, Castle!, Horse!, Skeams!, Heir!, Catalogues!, Sandy!, Quarantine!, Jeremy!, Spanish!, Inishleigh!, Mannin!

302. *Limonium humile* **Miller**   **Lax-flowered Sea-lavender, Lus liath na mara**

Locally common in saltmarshes.

Sherkin!, Heir!, Sandy (LCW 1982), Quarantine!, Jeremy!, Spanish!, Inishleigh!, Mannin!

OLEACEAE - ashes, privets and olives

303. *Fraxinus excelsior* **L.**   **Ash, Fuinseog**

An occasional hedgerow tree.

Sherkin (here and there between Abbey Strand and The Dock)!, Cape Clear!, Horse!, Heir!, Spanish!, Mannin!

304. *Ligustrum ovalifolium Hassk.*   **Japanese Privet, Pribhéad Seapánach**

Planted in gardens and as a hedge.

Sherkin!, Cape Clear!, Long!, Heir (LCW 1982).

GENTIANACEAE - centauries and gentians

305. *Cicendia filiformis* **(L.) Delarbre**   **Yellow Centaury, Deagha buí**

Locally common on damp, open, peaty and gravelly ground, often near the sea.

Sherkin!, Cape Clear!, W & M Calf!, Long!, Castle!, Horse!, Skeam W!, Heir!

Also on Ringarogy Island (JRA & DAW 1987). A speciality of the flora of West Cork and Kerry.

306. *Centaurium erythraea* **Rafn**   **Common Centaury, Dréimire Mhuire**

Heathland and short, dry or damp grassland near the sea.

Sherkin!, Cape Clear!, Calfs!, Long!, Castle!, Horse!, Skeams!, Heir!, Catalogues!, Sandy!, Quarantine!, Jeremy!, Spanish!, Inishleigh!, Mannin!

Variable in habit. A white-flowered variant occurs on Long.

307. *Centaurium pulchellum* **(Swartz) Druce**   **Slender Centaury, Dréimire beag**

Very rare in damp grassland near the sea. **Irish Red Data Book - Vulnerable.**

Cape Clear (J. Drummond 1818 in Colgan & Scully 1898), Horse (E. end, LCW 1982, BM & MWR 1995)!

We were unable to relocate this species in 1990-94, and the 1995 record is encouraging. Until then, L.C. Wright's specimen in the Sherkin herbarium had represented the only recent record from Co. Cork (Akeroyd & Clarke 1993). These are apparently the first records from Roaringwater Bay since 1818. Slender Centaury, a denizen of Dublin's North Bull Island, has recently been rediscovered at several old stations in Co. Wexford.

Allin (1883) dismissed Drummond's 1818 record from Cape Clear: "The var. *pulchella*, (*E. pulchella*, Fries) ... an error, as the true *E. pulchella* has only been observed on the east coast of Ireland." Polunin (1949) reported an "untypical form" of this species from Sherkin (Trabawn). The habitat at Trabawn would be suitable, but the record was not included in Polunin's published account (Polunin 1950), suggesting a change of thought, and intensive searches since 1986 have failed to find it there.

308. *Gentianella campestris* **(L.) Borner**   **Field Gentian, Lus an chrúbáin**

Grassland; flowers August to October.

Horse (Polunin 1950).

We have been unable to refind this attractive plant, mostly western and northern in Ireland, which has apparently declined elsewhere, for example on Clare Island (Doyle & Foss 1986).

MENYANTHACEAE - bog beans

309. *Menyanthes trifoliata* **L.**   **Bogbean, Báchrán**

Lake-margins, ponds and bog-pools; a fine sight in flower.

Sherkin!, Cape Clear!, Long!, Spanish!

APOCYNACEAE - periwinkles and oleanders

***310.** *Vinca major* **L.**   **Greater Periwinkle, Fincín mór**

Roadside banks as an occasional escape from gardens.

Sherkin!, Cape Clear!

RUBIACEAE – bedstraws

311. *Sherardia arvensis* **L.**   **Field Madder, Dearg faille**

Rather rare on grassy walls by the sea.

Sherkin!, Cape Clear!, E Calf!, Horse!, Heir!

312. *Galium palustre* **L.**   **Marsh Bedstraw, Rú corraigh**

Frequent in marshes.

Sherkin!, Cape Clear!, Calfs!, Long!, Castle!, Horse!, Skeam E!, Heir!, Catalogues!, Sandy!, Spanish!, Mannin!

313. *Galium verum* **L.**   **Lady's Bedstraw, Boladh cnis**

Locally common in coastal grassland and on walls and dry banks.

Sherkin!, Calfs!, Carthys!, Long!, Castle!, Horse!, Skeams!, Heir!, Catalogues!, Sandy!, Mannin!

314. *Galium saxatile* **L.**   **Heath Bedstraw, Luibh na bhfear gonta**

Common on dry heathland.

Sherkin!, Cape Clear!, W Calf (LCW 1982), M Calf!, Long!, Castle!, Horse!, Skeams!, Heir!, Catalogues!, Sandy!, Spanish!, Mannin!

Records of Hedge Bedstraw (*G. mollugo* L.), a very local plant in Ireland, from Cape Clear need confirmation. It was reported in West Cork only in 1994 (O'Mahony 1995).

315. *Galium aparine* **L.**   **Goosegrass, Garbhlus**

Common on walls, hedgerows and waste ground; sometimes on shingle strands and cultivated land.

Sherkin!, Cape Clear!, Calfs!, Goat!, Long!, Castle!, Horse!, Skeams!, Heir!, Catalogues!, Quarantine!, Spanish!, Mannin!

Prostrate, mostly rather compact plants with large fruits from shingle strands on Sherkin, Middle Calf, Long, Skeam East and Heir may belong to var. *maritimum* Fries.

316. *Rubia peregrina* **L.**   **Wild Madder, Garbhlus na Boirne**

Rare in hedges and scrub.

Sherkin (several stations at E. end)!, Cape Clear (RAP 1896, Polunin 1950), E Calf (NR 1993)!, Castle (NR 1993)!

A local plant in Ireland. It has been recorded on Sherkin from time to time since its discovery by Polunin (1949). N. Rowe's records greatly extend the known range in Roaringwater Bay.

HYDROPHYLLACEAE - phacelias

*317. *Phacelia tanacetifolia* **Benth.**   **Phacelia, Faicéilia**

Cape Clear (North Harbour, JRA 1994)!

Planted for ornament and becoming established on waste ground with various weeds and plants of coastal habitats, including Sea Storksbill. This North American plant is cultivated in Britain and Europe for green manure and to provide nectar for bees, and is becoming widely naturalised. McGough (1988) observed it at one coastal station in Co. Galway and noted a 1962 **DBN** specimen from Co. Down.

In 1995 a large patch of this plant appeared above South Harbour, Cape Clear, sown with other plants in a wildflower seed mixture. It is likely to become an established member of the flora.

CONVOLVULACEAE - bindweeds

318. *Cuscuta epithymum* **(L.) L.**   **Dodder, Clamhán**

A rare parasite on gorse.

Sherkin (RAP 1901; O'Donovan & O'Regan 1952; MB 1962), Heir (near East Pier, reported by local people up until c. 1987).

Rare in West Cork, perhaps introduced with clover seed (Power 1845).

319. *Calystegia soldanella* (L.) R.Br. Sea Bindweed, Plúr an phrionsa

Occasional on sand-dunes and blown sand at the top of strands.

Sherkin (LCW 1982), Horse (PCH & MWR 1994)!, Heir (JRA 1994)!

"Lough Hyne and Mizen Head '96: rare - Phillips" (Praeger 1901).

320. *Calystegia sepium* (L.) R.Br. subsp. *sepium* Hedge Bindweed, Ialus fáil

Common in hedges and on road-verges and stone walls, often around abandoned habitations.

Sherkin!, Cape Clear!, W & E Calf!, Long!, Castle!, Horse!, Skeams!, Heir!, Catalogues!, Quarantine (LCW 1982), Spanish!

321. *Calystegia sepium* (L.) R. Br. subsp. *roseata* Brummitt

Hedges; usually in more sheltered places than the common subspecies.

Sherkin!, Cape Clear (T O'M 1993), Long!, Skeam E!, Inishleigh (BM 1995)!

This subspecies can be recognised by the downy or shortly hairy stems, flower-stalks and leaf-stalks. The flowers are pink with white stripes, whereas those of subsp. *sepium* are usually white.

Reported by T. O'Mahony (1992 and pers. comm. 1993) from several other localities on the south coast of West Cork, as far east as Ross Carbery. Widespread but local on the coasts of West Ireland and West Britain, northwards to Co. Antrim and the Firth of Clyde (R.K. Brummitt in Perring & Sell 1968, Wyse Jackson 1995).

322. *Convolvulus arvensis* L. Field Bindweed, Ainleog

Common on walls, hedges, disturbed ground and the upper part of shingle strands.

Sherkin!, Cape Clear!, W & M Calf!, Long!, Horse!, Skeam E!, Heir!, Spanish (LCW 1982).

BORAGINACEAE – comfreys and forget-me-nots

[*323. *Echium vulgare* L. Viper's Bugloss, Lus nathrach

Cape Clear (RAP 1896).

Probably introduced and now extinct. Perhaps native only on or near the eastern coasts of Ireland.]

*324. *Symphytum officinale* L. Common Comfrey, Compar

An occasional relic of cultivation.

Sherkin!, Long!

325. *Myosotis arvensis* (L.) Hill Field Forget-me-not, Lus míonla goirt

Cultivated and disturbed ground.

Sherkin!, Cape Clear!, M & E Calf!, Heir!

326. *Myosotis discolor* **Pers.**   **Changing Forget-me-not, Lus míonla buí**

Local on dry banks and in sandy fields; sometimes in hay-meadows.

Sherkin!, Cape Clear!, Castle!, Horse!, Heir!

Records of Early Forget-me-not (*M. ramosissima* Rochel) from Sherkin and East Calf may refer to this species.

327. *Myosotis secunda* **A. Murray**   **Creeping Forget-me-not, Ceotharnach reatha**

Streams and marshy ground.

Sherkin!, Cape Clear!, M & E Calf!, Long!, Castle!, Skeam E!, Heir!, Spanish!

328. *Myosotis laxa* **Lehm. subsp.** *caespitosa* **(C.F. Schultz) Hyl. ex Nordh.**
(*M. caespitosa* **C.F. Schultz)**

                                                       Tufted Forget-me-not, Ceotharnach beag

Wet places.

Sherkin!, Cape Clear!, M & E Calf!, Long!, Castle (PW 1975), Horse!, Mannin (LCW 1982).

329. *Myosotis scorpioides* **L.**   **Water Forget-me-not, Ceotharnach uisce**

Wet places.

Sherkin!, Cape Clear!, M & E Calf!, Mannin (LCW 1982).

VERBENACEAE - vervains and lantanas

*330. *Verbena officinalis* **L.**   **Vervain, Beirbhéine**

Sherkin (Polunin 1949).

CALLITRICHACEAE - water-starworts

331. *Callitriche stagnalis* **Scop.**   **Common Water-starwort, Réiltín uisce**

Pools, streams and roadside runnels.

Sherkin!, Cape Clear!, Calfs!, Long!, Castle!, Horse!, Skeam E!, Heir!, Spanish!, Mannin (LCW 1982).

332. *Callitriche platycarpa* **Kütz**   **Various-leaved Water-starwort, Réiltín leathan**

Pools.

Sherkin!, W & E Calf!

333. *Callitriche hamulata* **Kütz ex Koch**

                                        Intermediate Water-starwort, Réiltín meánach

Acid or somewhat brackish pools.

Sherkin!, Cape Clear (Central Bog, as *C. intermedia* Hoffm., OP, unpublished notes), Calfs!, Catalogues!

LABIATAE (LAMIACEAE) - deadnettles, mints, thymes and woundworts

The plants of this large family have a characteristic appearance. The leaves are in pairs and the flowers, each with a prominent 'lip', are grouped in whorls. Many of these plants release a scent when crushed - for example, the mints and thymes. The family contains many garden herbs and medicinal plants. The flowers are attractive to bees and other insects.

334. *Ajuga reptans* **L.**   **Bugle, Glasair choille**

Grassy banks.

Sherkin (near school, HJL 1979; above Rugher Strand, PCH & MWR 1994)!, Cape Clear!, Castle!, Spanish!

335. *Teucrium scorodonia* **L.**   **Wood Sage, Iúr sléibhe**

Frequent on heathy banks and grassy walls.

Sherkin!, Cape Clear!, Long!, Castle!, Horse!, Skeams!, Heir!, Spanish!, Inishleigh!, Mannin!

"Wild Sage" was used in the islands to treat internal injuries (O'Reilly 1994).

336. *Scutellaria galericulata* **L.**   **Skullcap, Cochall**

Wet places.

Spanish!

337. *Scutellaria minor* **Huds.**   **Lesser Skullcap, Cochall beag**

Local in boggy places and damp heaths.

Sherkin (Foardree)!, Cape Clear!, M & E Calf!, Long!, Castle!, Heir!, Sandy!, Spanish!, Mannin!

338. *Galeopsis bifida* **Boenn.**   **Lesser Henbit, Ga buí**

Cultivated and disturbed ground.

Sherkin (as *G. tetrahit* L., Polunin 1949), Cape Clear!

339. *Lamium hybridum* **Vill.**   **Cut-leaved Dead-nettle, Caochneantóg dhiosctha**

Local and sporadic on cultivated ground; sometimes on shingle strands.

Sherkin!, Cape Clear!, M Calf!, Carthys!, Long!, Castle (confirming record, as *L. incisum*, of Allin 1883)!, Horse!, Skeam E!, Heir!

Red Deadnettle (*L. purpureum* L.) has been reported from Sherkin, perhaps in error for this species.

340. *Lamium amplexicaule* **L.**   **Henbit Dead-nettle, Caochneantóg chirce**

Rare on cultivated land.

Sherkin (Allin 1883), Cape Clear (N. of East Bog, JRA & KC 1992)!, Heir (Polunin 1949).

Also reported by Allin (1883) from Bro[w] Head and Toe Head on the mainland; Colgan & Scully (1898) recorded it as abundant in potato fields between Goleen and Schull.

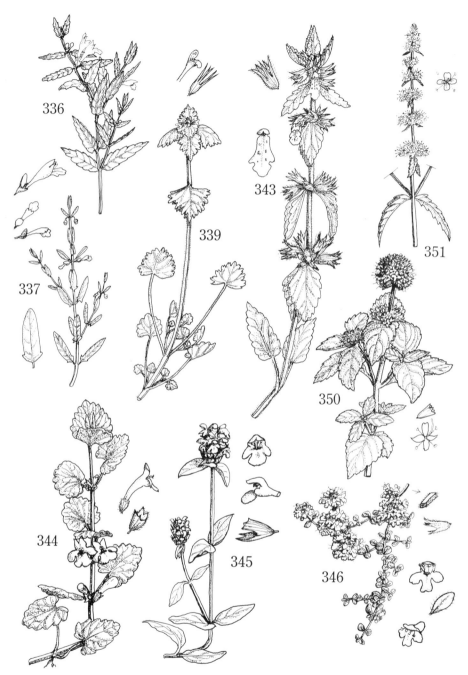

Mint family:

336 Skullcap

337 Lesser Skullcap

339 Cut-leaved Dead-nettle

343 Field Woundwort

344 Ground-ivy

345 Selfheal

346 Wild Thyme

350 Water Mint

351 Whorled Mint

341. *Stachys sylvatica* L.   **Hedge Woundwort, Créachtlus**

Local on shady lanesides and abandoned cultivated ground.

Sherkin!, W Calf!, Horse!, Skeam W!, Spanish!, Mannin!

Curiously scarce in its distribution in the islands and perhaps introduced.

342. *Stachys palustris* L.   **Marsh Woundwort, Cabhsadán**

A common plant of damp fields, lanesides and cultivated ground.

Sherkin!, Cape Clear!, Calfs!, Long!, Castle!, Horse!, Skeams!, Heir!, Catalogues (LCW 1982), Spanish!, Inishleigh!, Mannin!

343. *Stachys arvensis* (L.) L.   **Field Woundwort, Cuislín gan duaire**

Cultivated ground; sometimes on rock outcrops or shingle strands.

Sherkin!, Cape Clear!, Long!, Horse (confirming *Polunin 181*, 8.1948, **BM**)!, Skeam E!, Heir!, Catalogues!

344. *Glechoma hederacea* L.   **Ground-ivy, Athair lusa**

Shady places, often under bracken.

Sherkin!, Cape Clear!, E Calf!, Long!, Castle!, Horse!, Skeam W (LCW 1982), Heir!, Sandy!, Spanish!, Mannin!

345. *Prunella vulgaris* L.   **Selfheal, Duán ceannchosach**

Frequent in grassland.

Sherkin!, Cape Clear!, Calfs!, Long!, Castle!, Horse!, Skeams!, Heir!, Catalogues!, Sandy!, Spanish!, Inishleigh!, Mannin!

A dwarf variant grows on Horse in short, damp grassland by the sea.

346. *Thymus praecox* Opiz subsp. *arcticus* (Durand) Jalas

         Wild Thyme, Tím chreige

Rock outcrops in coastal grassland and heathland.

Sherkin!, Cape Clear!, Calfs!, Carthys!, Long!, Castle!, Horse!, Skeams!, Heir!, Catalogues!, Sandy!, Jeremy!, Spanish!, Inishleigh!

347. *Lycopus europaeus* L.   **Gypsywort, Feorán corraigh**

Sherkin (Tramore; Sherkin Point, LCW 1982)!, E Calf!, Spanish!

Also recorded from Goleen (RAP 1896).

[348. *Mentha pulegium* L.   **Pennyroyal, Borógach**

Probably extinct. **Irish Red Data Book - Vulnerable.**

Sherkin (Polunin 1949).

Also "on an island in Schull Bay" (Allin 1883), and at Goleen (Phillips in Praeger 1901).]

349. *Mentha arvensis* L.   **Corn Mint, Mismín arbhair**

Pastures and disturbed ground, often near houses.

Sherkin (O'Connor's field; Poulacurra, LCW 1982)!, Cape Clear (confirming record of Sharrock 1965)!, M Calf!, E Calf (LCW 1982), Long!, Horse!, Skeams!, Heir!, Catalogues!, Spanish!

350. *Mentha aquatica* L.   **Water Mint, Mismín mionsach**

Wet places and roadside runnels.

Sherkin!, Cape Clear!, M & E Calf!, Long!, Horse!, Skeams!, Heir!, Catalogues (LCW 1982), Sandy!, Spanish!, Mannin!

351. *Mentha x verticillata* L. (*M. aquatica x arvensis*)   Whorled Mint, Mismín burla

Wet places.

Sherkin (Polunin 1950), Horse!, Skeam E!

The commonest wild hybrid mint, both in the islands and in Ireland.

*352. *Mentha x piperita* L. var. *piperita* (*M. aquatica x spicata*)

Peppermint, Lus an phiobair

Roadsides and near buildings.

Sherkin!, Cape Clear!, Long!, Horse!, Heir!

Widespread in Ireland, escaping from gardens; a clump in the Marine Station garden was brought from mainland Cork in 1990.

*353. *Mentha longifolia* (L.) Hudson   **Horse Mint, Mismín capaill**

Sherkin ("Tranaplous Bay [Silver Strand]", Polunin 1949).

Perhaps recorded in error for Spear Mint (see Stace 1991, p. 684).

*354. *Mentha spicata* L. (*M. viridis* L.)   **Spear Mint, Cartlainn gharraí**

Roadsides and old gardens.

Sherkin (Polunin 1950), Long!

*355. *Mentha x villosa* Hudson (*M. spicata x suaveolens* Ehrh.)

Apple Mint, Mismín úill

Waysides and near ruins; garden escape.

Cape Clear (JRA & NR 1993)!, Castle (PCH & MWR 1994)!, Heir (LCW 1982, BM 1995)!

Wild Clary (*S. horminoides* Pourret) has been recorded from Sherkin in error, although long known (Allin 1883) from the Castle mound at Baltimore where it still flourished in 1993 (Wyse Jackson 1995). Another scarce member of the mint family, Calamint (*Calamintha sylvatica* Bromf. subsp. *ascendens* (Jordan) P.W. Ball & Heywood), also grows by the Castle at Baltimore (JRA 1995).

SOLANACEAE - nightshades and potatoes

This family gives us several major crops, notably the potato, tomato, aubergine and various peppers. Note that the green parts and usually the coloured berries are very poisonous.

*356. *Lycium barbarum* **L. (*L. chinense* auct., non Miller)**

Duke of Argyll's Teaplant, Lus an mhangaire

Occasionally cultivated as a hedge.

Sherkin!

*357. *Datura stramonium* **L.**   **Thorn-apple, Stoc an aingil**

Rare and sporadic on disturbed or cultivated ground.

Cape Clear (near Lough Errul, DB 1989).

Also recorded from Schull (O'Sullivan 1979a).

Native to tropical South America and a rare introduced plant in Ireland, with sporadic records over the last 30 years. However, it appeared in quantity in the warm late summer and autumn of 1978, and O'Sullivan (1979a, 1979b) reported 19 records, mostly from Co. Cork, including eight from West Cork. One population in a fodder beet crop near Ballinaspittle was estimated at 10,000 plants, many of them 2 m tall!

A very poisonous plant with dangerous narcotic properties. The species is famous for making a sudden appearance in late summer under warm weather conditions and can be headline news, as in Ireland during 1978.

SCROPHULARIACEAE – figworts, speedwells and toadflaxes

A varied family, with many familiar wild and garden flowers, such as Foxglove and the snapdragons. Several are weeds of cultivated ground.

358. *Verbascum thapsus* **L.**   **Great Mullein, Coinnle Muire**

Occasional, usually near houses or ruins; garden origin.

Sherkin (near Castle and church)!, Castle!, Horse!, Spanish!

*359. *Verbascum virgatum* **Stokes**   **Twiggy Mullein, Coinnle caola**

Spanish (O'Donovan & O'Regan 1952).

Phillips recorded this garden escape from Goleen (RAP 1896), and O'Donovan & O'Regan (1952) reported it from Baltimore, Skibbereen and a few other places in West Cork. O'Mahony (1975) gives a number of more recent Co. Cork records, noting that this plant "deserves a place in the Irish flora".

360. *Scrophularia nodosa* **L.**   **Common Figwort, Donnlus**

Lanes and hedge banks.

Sherkin!, Cape Clear!, Castle!, Horse!, Spanish!

361. *Scrophularia auriculata* **L. (*S. aquatica* auct.)**   **Marsh Figwort, Donnlus uisce**

Wet places and roadside ditches.

Sherkin!, Spanish!

362. *Misopates orontium* (L.) **Rafin.**   **Lesser Snapdragon, Srubh lao beag**

A rare and sporadic weed of cultivated and waste ground. **Irish Red Data Book - Vulnerable.**

Cape Clear (*O. Polunin 195*, 8.1948, **BM**; South Harbour, JRA & NR 1993; near East Pier, RF 1993)!

One of Ireland's most attractive wild plants but, like so many weeds, much reduced in numbers by modern agriculture. It has been recorded on Cape Clear from time to time over the last 30 years (records held at Bird Observatory, for example TC 1983).

363. *Cymbalaria muralis* **P. Gaertner, B. Meyer & Scherb.**

Ivy-leaved Toadflax, Buaflíon balla

Walls and bare, stony ground by roads, as an escape from cultivation.

Sherkin (including garden of Marine Station, recently established)!, Cape Clear (where it had been collected by Polunin in 1947-48)!, Heir!

364. *Kickxia elatine* (L.) **Dumort.**   **Sharp-leaved Fluellen, Buaflíon Breatnach**

Rare on cultivated and disturbed ground. **Irish Red Data Book - Vulnerable.**

Sherkin (Polunin 1949; Foardree, JRA & KC 1992; above Trabawn, PCH & MWR 1994))!, Cape Clear (RAP), Long (BM & MWR 1995)!, Horse (*O. Polunin 182*, 8.1948, **BM**; PCH & MWR 1994)! Skeam W (PCH & MWR 1994)!, Heir (BM & MWR 1995)!

A very rare plant in Ireland, now restricted to coastal districts of Mid and West Cork (O'Mahony 1985) and Co. Wexford and usually found on cultivated land. It was recently noted from barley fields near Castlefreke, West Cork (Wyse Jackson 1995). There is also a recent record from Co. Dublin (S. Reynolds, pers. comm.).

   At Foardree it occurs on open, peaty ground on a south-facing slope above the sea. The site may once have been cultivated when the island was more densely populated. The site on Skeam West is an eroding cliff at the top of the strand, probably once cultivated land. Phillips (in Praeger 1901) noted several localities and regarded Sharp-leaved Fluellen as frequent in West Cork; Polunin (1949) described it as "frequent on cultivated ground" on Sherkin; on Horse he collected it as a cornfield weed. The 1994-5 records suggest that this plant may still be quite widespread in the islands, perhaps coming up from buried seed.

365. *Digitalis purpurea* **L.**   **Foxglove, Lus mór**

Common amongst bracken, on roadsides, by walls and in low scrub.

Sherkin!, Cape Clear!, W Calf (LCW 1982), Long!, Castle!, Horse!, Skeams!, Heir!, Jeremy!, Spanish!, Inishleigh!, Mannin!

366. *Veronica serpyllifolia* **L.**   **Thyme-leaved Speedwell, Lus an treacha**

Damp, grassy places and by paths.

Sherkin!, Cape Clear!, E Calf!, Long!, Horse!, Skeam E!, Heir!

367. *Veronica officinalis* **L.**   **Heath Speedwell, Lus cré**

Heaths, banks and short grassland near the sea.

Sherkin!, Cape Clear!, Long!, Heir!, Spanish!

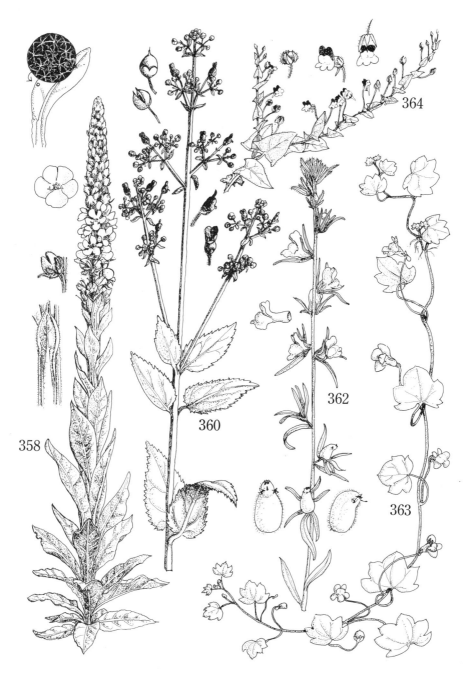

Mullein, Figwort and Snapdragon relatives:

358 Great Mullein

360 Common Figwort

362 Lesser Snapdragon

363 Ivy-leaved Toadflax

364 Sharp-leaved Fluellen

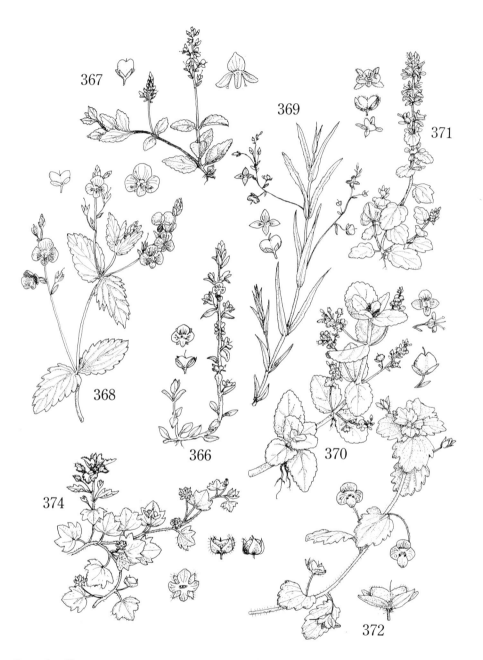

Speedwells:

366 Thyme-leaved Speedwell

367 Heath Speedwell

368 Germander Speedwell

369 Marsh Speedwell

370 Brooklime

371 Wall Speedwell

372 Common Field-speedwell

374 Ivy-leaved Speedwell

368. *Veronica chamaedrys* L. **Germander Speedwell, Anuallach**

Abundant on heathy banks, lanesides and rough grassland.

Sherkin!, Cape Clear!, M & E Calf!, Long!, Castle!, Horse (LCW 1982), Skeam E!, Heir!, Catalogues!, Sandy!, Spanish!, Mannin!

369. *Veronica scutellata* L. **Marsh Speedwell, Lus cré corraigh**

Wet places and beside loughs.

Sherkin (Farranacoush, *O. Polunin 248*, 8.1948, **BM**; Lough Ordree)!, Cape Clear (Sharrock 1965), Long!, Castle!, Heir!, Spanish!

Blue Water-speedwell (*V. anagallis-aquatica* L.) has been recorded from Sherkin and Castle, apparently in error for this species.

370. *Veronica beccabunga* L. **Brooklime, Lochall**

Wet ground and streams.

Sherkin!, Cape Clear!, M & E Calf!, Long!, Castle (LCW 1982), Horse!, Skeam E!, Heir!, Spanish (LCW 1982).

371. *Veronica arvensis* L. **Wall Speedwell, Lus cré balla**

Walls, dry banks and sand-dunes.

Sherkin!, Cape Clear!, E Calf!, Long!, Castle!, Horse!, Skeam E!, Heir!

Often small and inconspicuous, flowering early in the season, so probably overlooked.

372. *Veronica persica* **Poiret** **Common Field-speedwell, Lus cré garraí**

Cultivated and disturbed ground and waste places.

Sherkin!, Cape Clear!, Long!, Castle!, Heir!, Catalogues!, Sandy!, Mannin!

*373. *Veronica filiformis* **Sm.** **Slender Speedwell, Lus cré réileán**

Lawns and grassy places.

Sherkin (Murphy's Bar, JRA 1987-93; near school, JS 1990)!

A native of the Caucasus, introduced as a garden plant, that has spread through much of Ireland since it was first reported in 1933.

374. *Veronica hederifolia* **L. subsp.** *hederifolia*

Ivy-leaved Speedwell, Lus cré eidhneach

Very local on cultivated, bare and disturbed ground.

Sherkin (near church)!, Heir (by East Pier)!

This species was noticed only in 1994 and may be a recent introduction to the islands. It has a scattered distribution in Ireland and is rare in Co. Cork and the south-west.

*375. *Hebe x franciscana* **(Eastw.) Souster** **Hedge Veronica, Niamhscoth Phroinséis**

Cultivated for ornament and as a hedge-plant.

Sherkin!, Horse!

*376. *Hebe brachysiphon* **Summerh.**   **Hooker's Hebe, Niamhscoth Hooker**

Cultivated for ornament and as a hedge-plant; sometimes away from houses.

Sherkin!, Cape Clear!

Other Hebe (often known by botanists as *Parahebe*) species are grown in island gardens.

377. *Euphrasia arctica* **Lange ex Rostrup subsp.** *borealis* **(F. Towns.) Yeo**

Eyebright, Glanrosc

Common in meadows and on road-verges.

Sherkin!, Cape Clear!, Calfs!, Goat!, Long!, Castle!, Horse!, Skeam E!, Heir!, Sandy!, Jeremy!, Spanish!

378. *Euphrasia tetraquetra* **(Bréb.) Arrond.**   **Eyebright, Glanrosc**

Locally abundant in short maritime grassland.

Sherkin!, Cape Clear!, Calfs!, Long!, Castle!, Horse!, Skeam E!, Heir!, Sandy!, Spanish!

A distinctive plant of coastal grassland, with 4-sided inflorescences like miniature 'clock-towers'. Widespread around the coasts of Ireland and Britain.

379. *Euphrasia scottica* **Wettst.**   **Scottish Eyebright, Glanrosc caol**

Heathland near the sea.

Sherkin!, Cape Clear!, E Calf!, Goat!, Long!, Castle!, Heir!, Catalogues!, Sandy!

Local in Ireland, mainly in the west (Wyse Jackson 1995). Another eyebright, *E. confusa* Pugsley, is also recorded from Roaringwater Bay in Perring & Sell (1968).

380. *Odontites verna* **(Bellardi) Dumort. subsp.** *verna*   **Red Bartsia, Hocas tae**

Grassland and waysides

Sherkin!, Cape Clear!, Calfs!, Long!, Horse!, Skeam E!, Heir!, Catalogues!, Sandy!, Spanish!, Inishleigh (LCW 1982).

Some taller, more branched plants belong within subsp. *serotina* (Syme) Corb., which forms mixed populations with subsp. *verna* in the islands.

381. *Parentucellia viscosa* **(L.) Caruel**   **Yellow Bartsia, Hocas tae buí**

Damp grassland.

Sherkin!, Cape Clear!, Calfs!, Long!, Horse!, Skeam E!, Heir!, Catalogues!, Sandy!, Spanish!, Inishleigh (LCW 1982).

Also on Ringarogy Island (JRA & DAW 1987).

382. *Pedicularis sylvatica* **L. subsp.** *hibernica* **D.A. Webb**   **Lousewort, Lus an ghiolla**

Local in damp meadows and boggy places in heathland.

Sherkin!, Cape Clear!, Calfs!, Goat!, Long!, Castle!, Horse!, Skeam E!, Heir!, Catalogues!, Sandy!, Jeremy!, Spanish!, Mannin!

This subspecies, with hairy calyces, is the characteristic Irish plant; it has been discovered recently at a few localities in West Wales.

383. *Rhinanthus minor* L.   **Yellow-rattle, Gliográn**

Locally frequent in damp grassland, especially by the sea.

Sherkin!, Cape Clear!, Long!, Horse!, Skeam E!, Heir!, Catalogues & Sandy (LCW 1982), Spanish!

Some plants from Horse and elsewhere can be referred to subsp. *stenophyllus* (Schur) O. Schwarz, recorded from Roaringwater Bay in Perring & Sell (1968).

OROBANCHACEAE - broomrapes

384. *Orobanche minor* Sm.   **Common Broomrape, Múchóg bheag**

Very rare in pastures near the sea.

Sherkin (*O. Polunin*, 8.1948, **BM**; N.W. part of island, confirming records of HJL 1978, LCW 1982, KRB 1985)!, Horse (two stations at S. end, JRA & MWR 1994)!

Recently found on the mainland at Barley Cove (JRA & DAW 1987, O'Mahoney 1992, Wyse Jackson 1995). Allin (1883) noted it as a rare contaminent of clover seed in Co. Cork.

LENTIBULARIACEAE - butterworts and bladderworts

385. *Pinguicula lusitanica* L.   **Pale Butterwort, Leith uisce bheag**

Bogs.

Sherkin!, Cape Clear!, Long!, Heir!, Spanish!

386. *Pinguicula grandiflora* Lam.   **Large-flowered Butterwort, Leith uisce**

Damp, peaty ground by spring; not native on Sherkin, but a classic rarity of parts of Co. Cork and Kerry.

Sherkin (just south of Lough Ordree)!

Planted close to a garden. Some 20 plants survive several years after they were introduced.

387. *Utricularia vulgaris* L.   **Greater Bladderwort, Lus an bhorraigh**

Local but sometimes abundant in boggy pools.

Sherkin (Trabawn, Tramore)!, Cape Clear (Sharrock 1962), Long!

388. *Utricularia australis* R. Br. (*U. neglecta* Lehm.)   Bladderwort, Lus borraigh mór

Pools near the sea; perhaps now extinct.

Sherkin (Polunin 1949, 1950).

Good specimens of this plant from Trabawn, collected by Polunin and determined by R.D. Meikle and N.Y. Sandwith, and later by C.D. Preston, confirm this record (*O. Polunin* 8.1947, **K**; *O. Polunin 27*, 8.1948, **BM**); also a specimen from Farranacoush (*O. Polunin & P. Newbould* 67, 26.7.1949, **K**), determined by C.D. Preston.

PLANTAGINACEAE - plantains

389. *Plantago major* **L. subsp.** *major*   **Greater Plantain, Cuach Phádraig**

Common on open, trampled ground and disturbed grassland; tolerant of trampling.

Sherkin!, Cape Clear!, Calfs!, Carthys!, Long!, Castle!, Horse!, Skeams!, Heir!, Sandy!, Inishleigh!

The leaves were used in Western Ireland as dressings for wounds.

390. *Plantago major* **L. subsp.** *intermedia* **(DC.) Arcangeli**

Occasional on disturbed or cultivated ground; also by the harbour in Baltimore.

Sherkin (Marine Station and elsewhere)!, Cape Clear (North Harbour)!, Long!, Horse!, Heir!

Recognised by the hairy, 3- to 5-veined, somewhat toothed, pale green leaves and capsules with 12-18 or more seeds (5-9 in subsp. *major*). This variant has been largely overlooked in Ireland, although known to 19th Century botanists, but may be widespread (Brun-Hool & Wilmanns in White 1982, pp. 91-103; Akeroyd & Doogue 1988). It is a plant of cultivated land for the most part and does not tolerate trampling.

391. *Plantago coronopus* **L.**   **Buckshorn Plantain, Adharca fia**

Common on coastal rocks and dry, open ground near the sea.

Sherkin!, Cape Clear!, Bird!, Badger (LCW 1982), Calfs!, Carthys!, Goat!, Little Goat!, Long!, Castle!, Horse!, Skeams!, Heir!, Catalogues!, Sandy!, Quarantine!, Jeremy!, Spanish!, Inishleigh!, Mannin!

392. *Plantago maritima* **L.**   **Sea Plantain, Slánlus mara**

Common on coastal rocks, cliffs and saltmarshes.

Sherkin!, Cape Clear!, Badger!, Calfs!, Carthys!, Goat!, Little Goat!, Long!, Castle!, Horse!, Skeams!, Heir!, Catalogues!, Sandy!, Quarantine!, Jeremy!, Spanish!, Inishleigh!, Mannin!

393. *Plantago lanceolata* **L.**   **Lamb's-tongue Plantain, Slánlus**

Common in grassy and waste places and on cliffs.

Sherkin!, Cape Clear!, Calfs!, Carthys!, Goat!, Long!, Castle!, Horse!, Skeams!, Heir!, Catalogues!, Sandy!, Quarantine!, Jeremy!, Spanish!, Inishleigh!

A hairless, fleshy variant of this species occurs in exposed coastal grassland at the western end of Heir.

394. *Littorella uniflora* **(L.) Ascherson**   **Shoreweed, Lus an chladaigh**

Forming dense stands in shallow water of loughs and pools.

Sherkin (pool near Sherkin Point; BM 1995, confirming record of Polunin 1949)!, Cape Clear (Lough Errul, confirming record of RAP)!

114

CAPRIFOLIACEAE - honeysuckles and elders

395. *Sambucus nigra* **L.**   **Elder, Trom**

Scattered, mostly in hedges.

Sherkin!, Cape Clear!, Long!, Castle!, Horse!, Heir!

396. *Lonicera periclymenum* **L.**   **Honeysuckle, Féithleann**

Lanesides, hedges, roadside banks and sea-cliffs.

Sherkin!, Cape Clear!, Long!, Castle!, Horse!, Skeam E!, Heir!, Jeremy!, Spanish!, Inishleigh!, Mannin!

*397. *Lonicera nitida* **E. Wilson**   **Shining Honeysuckle, Féithleann geal**

Planted as a hedge.

Sherkin!

VALERIANACEAE - cornsalads and valerians

398. *Valerianella locusta* **(L.) Betcke**   **Common Cornsalad, Ceathrú uain**

Grassy walls and on ruins.

Sherkin (The Cross, PCH & MWR 1994)!

All the plants seen were dwarf and compact and belonged within var. *dunensis* D.E. Allen, scattered around the coasts of Ireland and Britain, mostly on sand-dunes. Hart (1898), writing of this variety in Co. Donegal, commented: "... it is a dainty, compact little plant, seldom more than one inch or two in height, much-branched and very floriferous.". Like other early-flowering annuals of walls and sand-dunes, this plant may be overlooked in the islands.

[*399. *Valerianella dentata* **(L.) Pollich   Narrow-fruited Cornsalad, Ceathrú uain chaol**

Cultivated land, especially potato fields; almost certainly extinct.

Sherkin (Polunin 1949).

A rare and decreasing plant in Ireland and Britain, but noted by Phillips as frequent at Baltimore (in Praeger 1901). Excellent specimens, with a distinctive, tall habit and long, narrow fruits, confirm this record (*O. Polunin 20*, 8.1947, **BM**).]

DIPSACACEAE - scabious

Wild scabious are the food plants of the caterpillars of the Marsh Fritillary. A thriving colony of these scarce butterflies lives on Sherkin.

400. *Succisa pratensis* **Moench**   **Devil's-bit Scabious, Odhrach bhallach**

Common in grassland and heathland. Flowering August to October.

Sherkin!, Cape Clear!, Calfs!, Goat!, Long!, Castle!, Horse!, Skeams!, Heir!, Catalogues!, Sandy!, Quarantine!, Jeremy!, Spanish!, Inishleigh!, Mannin (LCW 1982).

A white-flowered variant occurs on Spanish (MWR 1994).

401. *Knautia arvensis* **(L.) Coulter**   **Field Scabious, Cab an ghasáin**

Local on grassy banks.

Sherkin!, Long!, Castle (LCW 1982), Horse!, Skeam E!, Heir!, Sandy (LCW 1982).

CAMPANULACEAE - bellflowers

402. *Jasione montana* **L.**   **Sheep's-bit, Duán na gcaorach**

Common on dry banks, heathland, rock outcrops and walls.

Sherkin!, Cape Clear!, Calfs!, Goat!, Long!, Castle!, Horse!, Skeams!, Heir!, Catalogues!, Quarantine!, Jeremy!, Spanish!, Inishleigh!, Mannin!

Robust plants, for example, on the walls of Sherkin Abbey, belong within var. *latifolia* Pugsley, recorded from coastal cliffs and hedgerows in south-west Britain and Ireland. A white-flowered variant occurs on Long.

COMPOSITAE – dandelions, daisies, ragworts and thistles

These are some of the most conspicuous of all wild flowers, especially in grasslands, on waysides and cultivated ground. Many have feathery fruits that are readily dispersed by the wind. The dandelion 'clock' is the most familiar of these.

403. *Eupatorium cannabinum* **L.**   **Hemp-agrimony, Cnáib uisce**

Locally common on damp ground or in hedge-banks and scrub.

Sherkin (Horseshoe Harbour to The Dock)!, Cape Clear (North Harbour and elsewhere)!, E Calf!, Long!, Castle!, Spanish!

404. *Solidago virgaurea* **L.**   **Goldenrod, Slat óir**

Heathland, hedge-banks and cliffs.

Sherkin!, Cape Clear!, Long!, Horse!, Skeam E!, Heir!, Spanish!, Inishleigh!, Mannin!

405. *Bellis perennis* **L.**   **Daisy, Nóinín**

Short grassland, especially by the sea.

Sherkin!, Cape Clear!, Calfs!, Carthys!, Long!, Castle!, Horse!, Skeams!, Heir!, Catalogues!, Sandy!, Spanish!, Inishleigh!, Mannin!

406. *Aster tripolium* **L.**   **Sea Aster, Luibh bhléine**

Occasional on coastal rocks and in saltmarshes.

Sherkin!, Badger (JRA 1992, NR 1993)!, Skeam W!, Heir!, Sandy!, Quarantine!, Jeremy!, Spanish!, Inishleigh!, Mannin!

407. *Gnaphalium uliginosum* **L.**   **Marsh Cudweed, Gnamhlus corraigh**

Widespread on damp ground, especially where it is open, trampled or disturbed.

Sherkin!, Cape Clear!, Calfs!, Long!, Castle!, Horse!, Heir!, Spanish (LCW 1982).

Daisy family and allies:

400 Devil's-bit Scabious   402 Sheep's-bit   406 Sea Aster   410 Common Fleabane

401 Field Scabious   404 Goldenrod   409 Elecampane

[***408.** *Anaphalis margaritacea* (L.) Bentham (*Antennaria margaritacea* R. Br.)

Pearly Everlasting, Catluibh phéarlach

Cape Clear.

A native of North America, reported as a garden escape in the early to mid-19th century (Power 1845, Allin 1883), but not seen recently.]

409. *Inula helenium* L. **Elecampane, Meacan aillinn**

Occasional near derelict houses and other buildings.

Sherkin (Castle)!, Cape Clear (several places, especially W. end)!, W Calf!, Long!, Heir!

A relic of former medicinal use in the treatment of coughs and chest complaints, also skin ailments. It was first reported nearly 250 years ago "in plenty on Cape-clear Island" by Dr C. Smith [1750] (Power 1845); recorded there by O'Donovan & O'Regan (1952). There is an old record from Toe Head on the mainland (Allin 1883).

410. *Pulicaria dysenterica* (L.) Bernh. **Common Fleabane, Lus buí na ndreancaidí**

Marshes, wet fields, ditches and roadsides.

Sherkin!, Cape Clear!, M & E Calf!, Heir!, Catalogues!, Sandy!, Inishleigh (LCW 1982).

411. *Bidens tripartita* L. **Trifid Bur-marigold, Scothóg leathan**

Damp ground.

Sherkin (above Horseshoe Harbour)!, E Calf (BM 1995)!

*412. *Anthemis arvensis* L. **Corn Chamomile, Fíogadán goirt**

Disturbed ground; probably introduced with wildflower seed.

Cape Clear (above South Harbour, JRA & BM 1995)!

413. *Anthemis cotula* L. **Stinking Chamomile, Fínéal madra**

Cape Clear (Sharrock 1965).

414. *Achillea millefolium* L. **Yarrow, Athair thalún**

Common in grassland, road-verges, fields and waste places.

Sherkin!, Cape Clear!, Calfs!, Carthys!, Goat!, Long!, Castle!, Horse!, Skeams!, Heir!, Catalogues!, Sandy!, Quarantine (LCW 1982), Spanish!, Inishleigh!, Mannin!

415. *Chamaemelum nobile* (L.) All. (*Anthemis nobilis* L.) **Chamomile, Camán meall**

Heathland near the sea, often forming extensive mats or 'lawns'.

Sherkin!, Cape Clear!, Calfs!, Little Goat (NR 1993)!, Long!, Castle!, Horse!, Skeams!, Heir!, Catalogues!, Spanish!, Inishleigh (LCW 1982).

Also on adjacent mainland and Ringarogy Island (JRA & DAW 1987). Described as "abundant" by Polunin (1949), but rather local today on Sherkin.

416. *Tripleurospermum maritimum* (L.) Koch (*Matricaria maritima* L. subsp. *maritima*)

Sea Mayweed, Lus Bealtaine

Shingle strands, coastal rocks, sea-cliffs and bird islands; grassland and open ground by the sea.

Sherkin!, Cape Clear!, Bird!, Badger!, Calfs!, Carthys!, Goat!, Little Goat!, Long!, Castle!, Horse!, Skeams!, Heir!, Catalogues!, Sandy!, Quarantine!, Jeremy!, Spanish!, Inishleigh!, Mannin!

There are unconfirmed records of Scentless Mayweed (*T. inodorum* (L.) Schultz-Bip., *T. maritimum* subsp. *inodorum* (L.) Hyl. ex Vaar., *Matricaria inodora* L.) from the islands.

417. *Matricaria recutita* L. (*Chamomilla recutita* (L.) Rauschert)

Scented Mayweed, Fíogadán cumhra

Rare weed of cultivated and disturbed land.

Cape Clear (Polunin 1950; near South Harbour, JRA & NR 1993; JRA & BM 1995)!

*418. *Matricaria discoidea* DC. (*M. matricarioides* (Less.) Porter, *Chamomilla suaveolens* (Pursh) Rydb.)

Pineappleweed, Lus na hiothlann

Open, trampled ground, especially field gateways and lanes.

Sherkin!, Cape Clear!, M & E Calf!, Carthys (LCW 1982), Long!, Castle!, Horse!, Skeam W (LCW 1982), Skeam E!, Heir!

Probably originally from North America, this cosmopolitan weed was reported on Sherkin by Polunin (1949). First recorded in Britain in 1871 and Ireland in 1894, it spread over much of these islands in the first quarter of this century.

419. *Chrysanthemum segetum* L.   **Corn Marigold, Buíán**

Rare on cultivated land.

Cape Clear (south of Foilcoagh Bay, LCW 1982; near East Bog, JRA & KC 1992; above South Harbour, JRA & BM 1995)!

A relic of the ancient weed flora of the islands. Fields infested with this plant on Cape Clear were visible from a great distance as patches of gold.

420. *Tanacetum vulgare L.*   **Tansy, Franclus**

Sherkin (near Post Office)!

Surprisingly rare in the islands; long used in Co. Cork and elsewhere as a herb, both in medicine and for flavouring food, for example, drisheen.

*421. *Tanacetum parthenium* (L.) Schultz-Bip.   **Feverfew, Lus deartán**

Sherkin (Polunin 1949).

No longer apparently present on Sherkin, even as a garden plant, but still grown in a garden on Long (BM & MWR 1995).

Daisy family:

405 Daisy

407 Marsh Cudweed

411 Trifid Bur-marigold

414 Yarrow

415 Chamomile

416 Sea Mayweed

418 Pineappleweed

422 Oxeye Daisy

422. *Leucanthemum vulgare* **Lam.**   **Oxeye Daisy, Nóinín mór**

Hay-meadows, waysides and grassy walls.

Sherkin!, Cape Clear!, Calfs!, Long!, Horse!, Heir!, Sandy!, Jeremy!, Inishleigh!

423. *Artemisia vulgaris* **L.**   **Mugwort, Mongach meisce**

Rare, usually near houses and ruins.

Sherkin (Polunin 1949), Cape Clear!, Long!, Horse!, Heir!

424. *Artemisia absinthium* **L.**   **Wormwood, Mormónta**

Local near houses and ruins; also by the Castle at Baltimore.

Sherkin (RAP 1896, MB 1962, PW 1976; beyond Jolly Roger, JRA & SLJ 1986, JRA and others 1992-5)!, Cape Clear!, M Calf!, Skeams!, Heir!

First reported from Cape Clear by J. Drummond (Power 1845, Allin 1883). Formerly widely recorded but now a rare plant in Ireland, sparingly along the western coasts (for example, Connemara, *fide* JRA 1981). Scully (1916) noted it to be rare and decreasing in Co. Kerry.

O'Reilly (1994) notes that this aromatic plant was used on the islands to cure a bad stomach. It is tempting to suggest that it was also used as a flavouring for poteen, in the same way that it is used on Crete to flavour raki, the local spirit.

425. *Tussilago farfara* **L.**   **Colt's-foot, Sponc**

Eroding, low clayey cliffs by the sea.

Sherkin (Silver Strand)!, Cape Clear!, Long (near pier)!, Horse!, Heir (*O. Polunin*, 8.1947, **BM**; BM & MWR 1995)!

426. *Senecio jacobaea* **L.**   **Ragwort, Buachalán buí**

Widespread and often abundant in pastures, heaths and waysides.

Sherkin!, Cape Clear!, Calfs!, Carthys!, Little Goat!, Long!, Castle!, Horse!, Skeams!, Heir!, Sandy!, Catalogues!, Quarantine (LCW 1982), Jeremy!, Spanish!, Inishleigh!

Especially characteristic of overgrazed pastures. In 1992 it was very abundant on Sherkin and in places was being stripped by the larvae of the Cinnabar Moth. In 1993 it was very rare and larvae were seen feeding on Groundsel, although in that year Ragwort was still common on Long. It was common again in 1995 on Sherkin.

All the plants in the islands have rayed flowers. Rayless plants (subsp. *dunensis* (Dumort.) Kadereit & Sell) are common around much of the Irish coast, including Kerry.

427. *Senecio sylvaticus* **L.**   **Heath Groundsel, Grúnlas móna**

Rock outcrops, banks and bare places in heathy ground.

Sherkin (Polunin 1949), Cape Clear!, E Calf!, Heir!, Jeremy!, Inishleigh!

Also on Ringarogy Island (JRA & DAW 1987).

428. *Senecio vulgaris* **L.**   **Groundsel, Grúnlas**

Cultivated and disturbed ground.

Sherkin!, Cape Clear!, Badger!, Calfs!, Long!, Castle!, Horse!, Skeams!, Heir!, Catalogues (LCW 1982), Spanish!

*429. *Olearia macrodonta* Baker   Olearia, Oiléiria

Planted for shelter and ornament.

Sherkin (near Jolly Roger)!, Cape Clear!, Heir!

Another species, Daisybush (*O. x haastii* Hooker), is grown in gardens in the islands.

430. *Arctium minus* Bernh. subsp. *minus*   Lesser Burdock, Cnádán

Waysides and around farm buildings.

Sherkin!, Cape Clear!, E Calf!, Long!, Castle!, Horse!, Heir!

431. *Carduus tenuiflorus* Curtis   Slender Thistle, Feochadán caol

Waste ground and strands.

Sherkin (near harbour)!, Cape Clear (South Harbour)!, Calfs!, Long!, Castle!, Horse!, Skeams!, Spanish!

Welted Thistle (*C. acanthoides* L.) has been recorded from the islands, perhaps in error for this species.

432. *Cirsium vulgare* (Savi) Ten.   Common Thistle, Feochadán colgach

Pastures, waysides, shingle strands and disturbed ground.

Sherkin!, Cape Clear!, Calfs!, Carthys!, Goat!, Long!, Castle!, Horse!, Skeams!, Heir!, Catalogues!, Spanish!, Inishleigh!

433. *Cirsium palustre* (L.) Scop.   Marsh Thistle, Feochadán corraigh

Marshy ground and damp fields.

Sherkin!, Cape Clear!, Calfs!, Long!, Castle!, Horse!, Skeams!, Heir!, Catalogues!, Sandy!, Spanish!, Inishleigh!, Mannin!

Only the purple-flowered variant occurs on the islands, although it has been suggested that, on the coasts of South Wales at least, the white-flowered variant is at a selective advantage under conditions of exposure on coastal cliffs (Mogford 1974).

434. *Cirsium arvense* (L.) Scop.   Creeping Thistle, Feochadán reatha

Overgrazed fields, former cultivated land, waysides and shingle strands.

Sherkin!, Cape Clear!, Calfs!, Carthys!, Goat!, Long!, Castle!, Horse!, Skeams!, Heir!, Sandy!, Spanish!, Inishleigh!

435. *Centaurea nigra* L.   Hardheads, Mínscoth

Grassland and coastal heathland.

Sherkin!, Cape Clear!, Calfs!, Carthys!, Long!, Castle!, Horse!, Skeams!, Heir!, Catalogues!, Sandy!, Spanish!, Inishleigh!

*436. *Centaurea cyanus* **L.**   **Cornflower, Gormán**

Disturbed ground; probably introduced with wildflower seed.

Cape Clear (above South Harbour, JRA & BM 1995)!

[*437. *Cichorium intybus* **L.**   **Chicory, Siocaire**

Apparently extinct; probably introduced with fodder.

Cape Clear (RAP 1896).

Not refound by Polunin (1950), although it occurs today on Sherkin in at least one garden and may escape.]

438. *Hypochoeris radicata* **L.**   **Cat's-ear, Cluas chait**

Grassland, coastal heaths and grassy walls; flowering mostly in early summer.

Sherkin!, Cape Clear!, Calfs!, Goat!, Long!, Castle!, Horse!, Skeams!, Heir!, Catalogues!, Sandy!, Quarantine!, Jeremy!, Spanish!, Inishleigh!, Mannin!

439. *Leontodon autumnalis* **L.**   **Autumn Hawkbit, Crág phortáin**

Common in grassland and rocky or open ground; flowering during late summer and autumn.

Sherkin!, Cape Clear!, Badger!, Calfs!, Carthys!, Long!, Castle!, Horse!, Skeams!, Heir!, Catalogues!, Sandy!, Spanish!, Inishleigh!, Mannin!

440. *Leontodon taraxacoides* **(Vill.) Merat (***L. leysseri* **(Wallr.) Beck.)**

Lesser Hawkbit, Crág phortáin bheag

Coastal grassland; flowering in early summer.

Sherkin!, Cape Clear!, Calfs!, Long!, Castle!, Horse!, Skeams!, Heir!, Sandy!, Spanish!, Inishleigh (LCW 1982).

The rather similar Rough Hawkbit (*L. hispidus* L.) has been reported from the islands, but needs confirmation. Phillips did not record this plant in West Cork (Praeger 1901), but there is a record from Roaringwater Bay in Perring & Walters (1976).

441. *Sonchus asper* **(L.) Hill**   **Prickly Sowthistle, Bleachtán colgach**

Common on waste ground and lanesides.

Sherkin!, Cape Clear!, Calfs!, Carthys!, Long!, Castle!, Horse!, Skeams!, Heir!, Catalogues!, Spanish!, Mannin!

442. *Sonchus oleraceus* **L.**   **Common Sowthistle, Bleachtán mín**

Widespread in cultivated and waste ground; frequently on walls of derelict buildings.

Sherkin!, Cape Clear!, Badger!, Calfs!, Long!, Castle!, Horse!, Skeams!, Heir!, Catalogues!, Inishleigh!

443. *Sonchus arvensis* **L.**   **Perennial Sowthistle, Bleachtán léana**

Common on road verges, waste ground and strands (rare on Cape Clear).

Sherkin!, Cape Clear (South Harbour)!, Calfs!, Long!, Castle (LCW 1982), Horse!, Skeam W (LCW 1982), Skeam E!, Heir!, Catalogues!, Sandy!, Quarantine (LCW 1982), Spanish!, Inishleigh!, Mannin!

Populations of Perennial Sowthistle at Silver Strand and at Trabawn, each near the top of the strand beside a small stream, differ by having hairless, rather than conspicuously glandular-hispid, peduncles and bracts. Some intermediate, sparsely hairy plants occur nearby. Whilst superficially similar to subsp. *uliginosus* (M. Bieb.) Nyman, an East European variant of this species formerly thought to occur in the British Isles (Lousley 1968), it differs by the single character and is best placed in var. *glabrescens* Hall (P.D. Sell, pers. comm.).

This variant has not been reported from Ireland in the literature, but two other Irish specimens have been seen by JRA: Burren, Co. Clare (*C.E. Raven*, 11.9.1955, **CGE**) and an almost hairless plant from a rocky seashore at Rostrevor, Co. Down (*S.A. Stewart*, 8.1882, **DBN**). A clone of var. *glabrescens* from Silver Strand and one of var. *arvensis* from elsewhere on Sherkin remained distinct in cultivation in the Harris Botanic Garden, University of Reading, for several years, so the hairless character has at least some genetic basis. It would be interesting to know whether this variant is subcoastal as the Irish records suggest.

444. *Taraxacum officinale* **Weber**   **Dandelion, Caisearbhán**

Grassland, sandy ground near the sea, cultivated ground, paths and waysides.

Sherkin!, Cape Clear!, Calfs!, Carthys!, Long!, Castle!, Horse!, Skeams!, Heir!, Catalogues!, Sandy!, Spanish!, Inishleigh!

No collections have been made to assess which 'microspecies' of dandelions may be present. An infusion of dandelion roots was used in the islands to treat rheumatism (O'Reilly 1994).

445. *Taraxacum laevigatum* **(Willd.) DC.**   **Lesser Dandelion, Caisearbhán**

Occasional on open, stony ground, blown sand or walls; probably under-recorded.

Sherkin!, Cape Clear!

446. *Lapsana communis* **L.**   **Nipplewort, Duilleog Bhríde**

Waysides, waste ground and as a garden weed.

Sherkin!, Cape Clear!, Long!, Horse!, Skeam E!, Heir!

447. *Crepis capillaris* **(L.) Wallr.**   **Smooth Hawk's-beard, Lus cúráin mín**

Grassland and waysides.

Sherkin!, Cape Clear!, Calfs!, Long!, Horse!, Skeam E!, Heir!, Catalogues (LCW 1982), Spanish!

448. *Crepis vesicaria* **L. subsp.** *taraxacifolia* **(Thuill.) Thell. ex Schinz & Keller (***C. vesicaria* **subsp.** *haenseleri* **(Boiss. ex DC.) P.D. Sell)**

Beaked Hawk's-beard, Lus cúráin gobach

Hay-meadows; first recorded on Sherkin in 1994 and perhaps introduced with grass-seed.

Sherkin (fields to west of church)!, Cape Clear (records held at Bird Observatory).

449. *Pilosella officinarum* **F. Schultz & Schultz Bip. (***Hieracium pilosella* **L.)**

Mouse-ear Hawkweed, Searbh na muc

Dry heathy ground, banks and wall-tops.

Sherkin!, Cape Clear!, E Calf!, Long!, Horse!, Skeam E!, Heir!, Sandy!, Spanish!

ALISMATACEAE - water-plantains

450. *Baldellia ranunculoides* **(L.) Parl.**   **Lesser Water-plantain, Corrchopóg bheag**
Peaty pools.

Sherkin!, Cape Clear!, M Calf!, Long!, Sandy (LCW 1982).

451. *Alisma plantago-aquatica* **L.**   **Water-plantain, Corrchopóg**
Pools and edges of loughs.

Sherkin!, Cape Clear!, M & E Calf!, Long!

JUNCAGINACEAE - arrow-grasses

452. *Triglochin maritima* **L.**   **Sea Arrowgrass, Barr an mhilltigh mara**
Common in saltmarshes.

Sherkin!, Cape Clear!, E Calf!, Long!, Skeam W!, Heir!, Catalogues!, Sandy!, Quarantine!, Jeremy!, Spanish!, Inishleigh!, Mannin!

453. *Triglochin palustris* **L.**   **Marsh Arrowgrass, Barr an mhilltigh**
Rather local in brackish marshes; a smaller, less robust plant.

Sherkin!, Cape Clear!, M Calf!, Long!, Horse!, Heir!, Spanish!, Mannin (LCW 1982).

POTAMOGETONACEAE – pondweeds

Pondweeds are leafy plants that grow submerged in loughs and rivers. Their small greenish flowers are massed in spikes that emerge above the water surface.

454. *Potamogeton natans* **L.**   **Broad-leaved Pondweed, Liach Bhríde**
Open water of loughs and pools.

Sherkin (Farranacoush, OP, unpublished notes; Trabawn, NS 1992; Lough Ordree)!, Cape Clear (Lough Errul)!, M & E Calf!, Long!, Heir (OP, unpublished notes), Spanish!

455. *Potamogeton polygonifolius* **Pourret**   **Bog Pondweed, Liach mhóna**
Peaty pools and wet bogs, especially in slowly running water.

Sherkin!, Cape Clear!, M & E Calf!, Long!, Horse!, Heir!, Spanish!

456. *Potamogeton obtusifolius* **Mert. & Koch**

Blunt-leaved Pondweed, Líobhógach mhaol
Cape Clear (Central Bog, JHB & JMW 1951 in Richards 1969).

457. *Potamogeton berchtoldii* **Fieber**   **Small Pondweed, Líobhógach bheag**
Peaty pools.

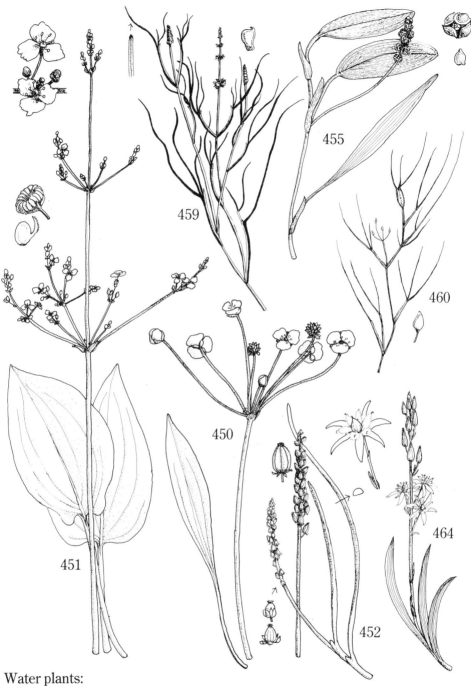

Water plants:

450 Lesser Water-plantain

451 Water-plantain

452 Sea Arrow-grass

455 Bog Pondweed

459 Fennel Pondweed

460 Beaked Tasselweed

464 Bog Asphodel

This weatherbeaten Monterey Cypress on Sherkin has withstood many a winter storm.

The lane to Sherkin Point: old trackways are a rich habitat for wild plants.

The ruins of Sherkin Abbey, dating from 1460, dominate the skyline
at the eastern end of the island.

On Cape Clear, the last stronghold of the O'Driscolls, Dun an Oir fell to the English in 1602.

Traditional farming has largely disappeared from the islands.

Photo: Ian Watts

Stone buildings and walls - and introduced plants - survive long after those who built them and moved on.

Photo: Ian Watts

The jagged ribs of Roaringwater Bay: rock strata on Middle Calf.

Farmer lazy beds show how widely the land was cultivated in past centuries.

Steeply tilted Old Red Sandstone rocks create dramatic cliffs on Cape Clear and Sherkin.

Photo: Ian Watts

Cape Clear is the backdrop to plant-rich grassland on blown sand and rocks at Cow Strand, Sherkin.

Photo: Paul Kay

The causeway on Heir links the wild, heathy western end of the island to the gentler landscape of the eastern part.

North Harbour, Cape Clear: the observant visitor will find interesting plants even on the harbour walls.

Ruined farms on West Calf: an evocative reminder of once-thriving island communities.

Abbey Strand: first landfall for the visitor to Sherkin.

Cape Clear (Central Bog, JHB & JMW 1951 in Richards 1969), M Calf (PCH & MWR 1994)!

There are specimens of both Blunt-leaved and Small Pondweed from Central Bog (oddly labelled Mid Fen!), Cape Clear, at Oxford (**OXF**, *fide* JRA). No trace of these two species was found during the present survey, which perhaps indicates habitat change since the early 1950s.

458. *Potamogeton crispus* **L.**   **Curled Pondweed, Líobhógach chatach**
Open water of loughs.

Sherkin (Lough Ordree, Polunin 1949; Tramore)!, Cape Clear (Sharrock 1965), M Calf!

459. *Potamogeton pectinatus* **L.**   **Fennel Pondweed, Líobhógach fhinéiliúl**
Pools near the sea.

Sherkin (confirming record of Polunin 1949)!, Cape Clear (East Bog)!, M & E Calf!, Skeam W!, Heir!, Spanish (LCW 1982).

A record of Various-leaved Pondweed (*P. gramineus* L.) from Sherkin probably refers to this plant. Fennel Pondweed has been confused with Beaked Tasselweed (see below).

RUPPIACEAE - tasselweeds

460. *Ruppia maritima* **L.**   **Beaked Tasselweed, Scothóga mara**
Brackish pools by the sea.

Sherkin (pool near Sherkin Point, PCH & MWR 1994, confirming record of Polunin 1949)!, W Calf (BM & MWR 1995)!

A 1994 specimen was determined by C.D. Preston, who noted that the leaf-tips of tasselweeds are minutely toothed, whereas those of similar, narrow-leaved pondweeds are entire. It was very abundant at both sites in 1995. This is a rare plant in Ireland, with most recent records from the west and north.

ZOSTERACEAE - eelgrasses

Eelgrasses are seaweed-like Flowering Plants that live successfully in the sea. Their strap-like leaves are sometimes washed up on strands.

461. *Zostera marina* **L.**   **Eelgrass, Miléarach**
Sublittoral zone; often abundant, forming great beds.

Sherkin!, Cape Clear (Edmunds 1960), Long!, Horse!, Skeams!, Heir!, Catalogues!, Sandy!

462. *Zostera angustifolia* **(Hornem.) Reichenb.**

Narrow-leaved Eelgrass, Miléarach chaol
Locally abundant in sublittoral zone; perhaps only a variety of Eelgrass.
Sherkin!, Horse!

463. *Zostera noltii* **Hornem.**   **Dwarf Eelgrass, Miléarach bheag**
Locally abundant in sublittoral zone.

Sherkin (Horseshoe Harbour, PK 1992)!

LILIACEAE - lilies, onions and garlic

The 1844 *Parliamentary Gazette* reported that the food of the inhabitants of Cape Clear consisted chiefly of "potatoes and fish boiled together, and seasoned with leeks, onions and garlic".

464.   *Narthecium ossifragum* (L.) Hudson   Bog Asphodel, Sciollam na móna

Bogs; rather local.

Sherkin!, Cape Clear!, Long!, Heir!, Spanish!

465.   *Hyacinthoides non-scripta* (L.) Chouard ex Rothm.   Bluebell, Coinnle corra

Heaths and banks, often under bracken.

Sherkin!, Cape Clear!, M & E Calf!, Carthys!, Goat!, Little Goat!, Castle!, Horse (LCW 1982), Skeams!, Heir!, Catalogues!, Sandy!, Jeremy!, Spanish!, Inishleigh!, Mannin!

A white-flowered variant occurs on Sherkin at low frequency (KC 1992).

*466. *Allium sativum* L.   Garlic, Gairleog

Field margins; a relic of cultivation.

Heir (near Restaurant, BM & MWR 1995)!

The only other Irish record of this plant is from Co. Sligo (Wyse Jackson 1995). The plants on Heir were not more than 100 cm tall, much smaller than Babington's Leek (see below).

467.   *Allium ampeloprasum* L. var. *babingtonii* (Borrer) Syme

Babington's Leek, Cainneann

Field-margin and garden of derelict house. Numbers range from 10 to 30 plants per year.

Sherkin (above road from church towards Sherkin Point, KC 1992; JRA 1993-5)!

This distinctive leek has long been known from the Aran Islands and the coasts of West Galway (Webb & Scannell 1983) and Donegal, with recent records reported from Co. Sligo and Co. Leitrim (Cotton & Cawley 1993). Also widespread in the Isles of Scilly and the coast of mainland Cornwall, it is considered to be a relic of ancient cultivation, probably introduced from the Mediterranean region where the species has its centre of distribution (Stearn 1978, but regarded by some botanists to be a native species - Webb & Scannell 1983). Var. *babingtonii*, found only in Western Ireland and South-Western England, is often associated with human habitation and old ruins. The Sherkin plants might have been introduced, but they do provide a geographical link between the two main areas of distribution of this plant.

Var. *babingtonii* is characterised by loose heads of flowers, with some secondary and even tertiary clusters, the flowers intermixed with rather large bulbils that enable the plant to reproduce vegetatively. Plants from the Channel Islands and other islands of the coast of north-west France with more compact heads of flowers and smaller bulbils belong to var. *bulbiferum* Syme. The cultivated Leek (*A. porrum* L.) was derived from this species and it is likely that Babington's Leek was formerly grown as a vegetable or flavouring. It is a remarkable cultural relic and should be considered to be a significant genetic resource. Wyse Jackson (1995) has noted that this plant is very similar to garden Garlic (*A. sativum* L.). The Sherkin plants are c. 2 m tall, with few leaves and purple perianth-segments that are shorter than the stamens. There is no doubt that they are Babington's Leek.

AGAVACEAE - agaves and New Zealand flaxes

*468. *Phormium tenax* **J.R. & G. Forster   New Zealand Flax, Líon na Nua-Shéalainne**

Cultivated for ornament and more or less escaping.

Sherkin!, Cape Clear!, Long!, Horse (recently planted)!, Heir!

This plant was once the basis of a fibre industry in the Dingle peninsula of Kerry.

IRIDACEAE - irises

469. *Iris pseudacorus* **L.   Yellow Flag, Feileastram**

Frequent in damp fields and marshy ground.

Sherkin!, Cape Clear!, M & E Calf!, Long!, Castle!, Horse!, Skeam E!, Heir!, Sandy!, Spanish!, Inishleigh!

*470. *Tritonia x crocosmiflora* **(Lemoine) Nicholson   Montbretia, Feileastram dearg**

Widely naturalised and often abundant and conspicuous on banks and walls.

Sherkin!, Cape Clear!, Long!, Skeams!, Heir!

JUNCACEAE – rushes

Rushes are characteristic plants of damp and overgrazed pastures, especially where there is trampling and soil compaction (poaching) by stock.

471. *Juncus maritimus* **Lam.   Sea Rush, Meathán mara**

Upper part of saltmarshes and margins of rocky pools by the sea.

Sherkin!, Cape Clear (Sharrock 1965), W & E Calf!, Long!, Castle!, Horse!, Skeams!, Heir!, Catalogues!, Sandy!, Quarantine (LCW 1982), Jeremy!, Spanish!, Inishleigh!, Mannin!

472. *Juncus effusus* **L.   Soft Rush, Geataire**

Poorly drained pastures.

Sherkin!, Cape Clear!, Calfs!, Goat!, Long!, Castle!, Horse!, Skeam W (LCW 1982), Skeam E!, Heir!, Catalogues!, Sandy!, Quarantine (LCW 1982), Jeremy!, Spanish!, Inishleigh!, Mannin!

Var. *subglomeratus* DC., with compact flower-heads, occurs on many of the islands.

473. *Juncus conglomeratus* **L.   Clustered Rush, Luachair dhlúth**

Poorly drained pastures.

Sherkin!, Cape Clear!, W Calf!, Long!, Horse!

474. *Juncus gerardi* **Loisel.   Saltmarsh Rush, Luachair mhuirisce**

Frequent in salt-marshes, on coastal rocks and the upper part of strands.

Sherkin!, Cape Clear!, Calfs!, Carthys!, Long!, Castle!, Horse!, Skeams!, Heir!, Catalogues!, Sandy!, Quarantine!, Jeremy!, Spanish!, Inishleigh!, Mannin!

475. *Juncus bufonius* **L.**   **Toad Rush, Buafluachair**

Bare, often damp ground.

Sherkin!, Cape Clear!, Badger!, Calfs!, Long!, Castle!, Horse!, Skeams!, Heir!, Catalogues!, Sandy!, Quarantine!, Spanish!, Inishleigh!, Mannin!

476. *Juncus bulbosus* **L.**   **Bulbous Rush, Luachair bhleibeach**

In and around peaty pools, often forming dense, floating mats.

Sherkin!, Cape Clear!, M & E Calf!, Long!, Castle (LCW 1982), Skeam E!, Heir!, Spanish!

477. *Juncus acutiflorus* **Ehrh. ex Hoffm.**   **Sharp-flowered Rush, Fiastalach**

Damp ground and poorly-drained pastures.

Sherkin!, Cape Clear!, Calfs!, Long!, Castle!, Horse!, Skeam E!, Heir!, Catalogues!, Sandy!, Spanish!, Inishleigh!, Mannin!

478. *Juncus acutiflorus x articulatus* **(*J. x surrejanus* Druce ex Stace & Lambinon)**

Cape Clear (Central Bog, Richards 1969).

479. *Juncus articulatus* **L.**   **Jointed Rush, Lachán na ndamh**

Marshes, often near the sea.

Sherkin!, Cape Clear!, Calfs!, Goat (LCW 1982), Long!, Castle!, Horse!, Skeams!, Heir!, Catalogues!, Sandy!, Quarantine (LCW 1982), Spanish!, Inishleigh!, Mannin!

480. *Luzula campestris* **(L.) DC.**   **Field Wood-rush, Giúnach léana**

Rare in short grassland of coastal heaths.

Sherkin!, Cape Clear!, Long!, Heir!

481. *Luzula multiflora* **(Retz.) Lej.**   **Heath Wood-rush, Giúnach caoráin**

Heathland.

Sherkin!, Cape Clear!, Calfs!, Goat!, Long!, Castle!, Horse!, Skeams!, Heir!, Catalogues!, Sandy!, Jeremy!, Spanish!, Inishleigh!, Mannin!

Polunin (1949) reported *L. multifora* var. *congesta* (Thuill.) Koch from Sherkin.

GRAMINEAE - grasses

Grasses are the commonest and most economically important group of wild and cultivated plants. The meadows and pastures in Roaringwater Bay show great variety and are an important natural resource. In summer they are bright with clovers, orchids and other flowers.

482. *Festuca pratensis* **Hudson**   **Meadow Fescue, Feisciú móinéir**

Grassland; probably overlooked.

Horse!, Heir!

483. *Festuca arundinacea* **Schreber**   **Tall Fescue, Feisciú ard**

Edge of cultivated fields.

Heir (W. end, BM 1995)!

484. *Festuca rubra* **L. subsp.** *rubra*   **Red Fescue, Feisciú rua**

Ubiquitous grass of a range of habitats.

Sherkin!, Cape Clear!, Bird!, Badger!, Calfs!, Carthys!, Goat!, Little Goat!, Long!, Castle!, Horse!, Skeams!, Heir!, Catalogues!, Sandy!, Quarantine!, Jeremy!, Spanish!, Inishleigh!, Mannin!

Polunin (1950) reported *F. rubra* var. *barbata* (Schrank) Richt. from cliffs on Heir. Greyish-leaved plants from cliffs and rocks by the sea grade into subsp. *pruinosa* (Hackel) Piper, not previously reported from West Cork.

*485. *Festuca nigrescens* **Lam. (*F. rubra* L. subsp.** *commutata* **Gaudin)**

                    Chewing's Fescue, Feisciú Chewing

Grassland; introduced forage grass.

Horse (LCW 1982).

486. *Festuca ovina* **L.**   **Sheep's Fescue, Feisciú caorach**

Heathland and rocky ground.

Sherkin!, Cape Clear!, Badger (NR 1993)!, Calfs!, Carthys!, Goat!, Little Goat!, Long!, Castle!, Horse!, Skeams!, Heir!, Catalogues!, Sandy!, Quarantine!, Jeremy!, Spanish!, Inishleigh!, Mannin!

487. *Lolium perenne* **L.**   **Perennial Rye-grass, Seagalach buan**

Grassland and widely sown in leys.

Sherkin!, Cape Clear!, Calfs!, Carthys!, Long!, Castle!, Horse!, Skeams!, Heir!, Catalogues!, Sandy!, Spanish!, Inishleigh!

*488. *Lolium multiflorum* **Lam.**   **Italian Rye-grass, Seagalach lodálach**

Improved grassland of pastures and hay-meadows.

Sherkin (Polunin 1950), Cape Clear!, Heir (field behind old schoolhouse, BM & MWR 1995, confirming record of Polunin 1950)!

[489. *Lolium temulentum* **L.**   **Darnel, Roille**

Cultivated fields; extinct. **Irish Red Data Book - Extinct**, but refound in the Aran Islands whilst that book was in press.

Sherkin (Polunin 1949).

An annual, arable weed that is almost extinct in Ireland, except in the Aran Islands (Curtis, McGough & Wymer 1988). Like Corn Cockle, it declined rapidly after 1945. This is the darnel or tare of Jesus' parable in Matthew 13, verses 24-30.]

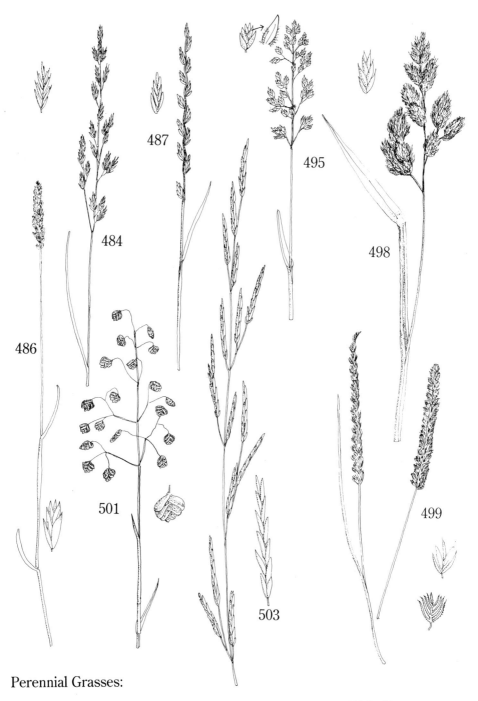

Perennial Grasses:

484 Red Fescue

486 Sheep's Fescue

487 Perennial Rye-grass

495 Spreading Meadow-grass

498 Cock's-foot

499 Crested Dog's-tail

501 Quaking-grass

503 Floating Sweet-grass

490. *Vulpia bromoides* (L.) S.F. Gray   **Squirreltail Brome, Feisciú aimrid**

Walls and rock outcrops near the sea.

Sherkin!, Cape Clear!, M & E Calf!, Long!, Horse!, Skeams!, Heir!, Catalogues!, Spanish!

491. *Vulpia myuros* (L.) C.C. Gmelin   **Rat's-tail Fescue, Feisciú balla**

Sherkin (Polunin 1949).

492. *Desmazeria marina* (L.) Druce (*Catapodium marinum* (L.) C.E. Hubbard)

Sea Fern-grass, Féar trá

Walls and rocks near the sea, sometimes on blown sand.

Sherkin!, Cape Clear!, Badger (NR 1993)!, W & M Calf!, E Calf (confirms record, as *Sclerochloa loliacea*, of Allin 1883)!, Carthys (LCW 1982), Long!, Castle!, Horse!, Skeam E!, Heir!, Catalogues!

493. *Poa annua* L.   **Annual Meadow-grass, Cuise bliantúil**

Common in cultivated ground, on waysides, lanes, rock outcrops and strands.

Sherkin!, Cape Clear!, Badger!, Calfs!, Long!, Castle!, Horse!, Skeams!, Heir!, Catalogues & Sandy (LCW 1982), Spanish!, Inishleigh (LCW 1982), Mannin!

Many plants on Sherkin, Cape Clear, Horse and probably elsewhere are perennial. Polunin (1950) recorded *P. annua* var. *reptans* Hausskn., which is likely to be the same plant.

494. *Poa trivialis* L.   **Rough Meadow-grass, Cuise garbh**

Damp grassland.

Sherkin!, Cape Clear!, W Calf (LCW 1982), M & E Calf!, Carthys!, Castle!, Horse!, Skeams!, Heir!, Mannin!

495. *Poa subcaerulea* Sm. (*P. irrigata* Lindm.) Spreading Meadow-grass, Cuise reatha

Coastal grassland, shingle strands and wall-tops.

Sherkin!, Cape Clear!, Calfs!, Carthys!, Little Goat!, Long!, Castle!, Horse!, Skeams!, Heir!, Catalogues!, Sandy!, Spanish!, Inishleigh!, Mannin!

This rather distinctive grass should perhaps best be treated as a subspecies of Smooth Meadow-grass. It is distinguished by the less tufted growth, stems not more than 40cm tall, and flowering branches in 2s and 3s (rather than clusters of 3-5).

496. *Poa pratensis* L.   **Smooth Meadow-grass, Cuise mín**

Common in meadows, pastures, verges of lanes and gardens.

Sherkin!, Cape Clear!, Calfs!, Carthys!, Goat!, Long!, Castle!, Horse!, Skeams!, Heir!, Catalogues!, Sandy!, Spanish!, Inishleigh!

497. *Puccinellia maritima* (Hudson) Parl.   **Common Saltmarsh-grass, Féar muirisce**

Saltmarshes, coastal rocks and sometimes on shingle strands.

Sherkin!, Cape Clear!, Bird!, Badger!, Calfs!, Carthys!, Long!, Castle!, Horse!, Skeams!, Heir!, Catalogues!, Sandy!, Quarantine!, Jeremy!, Spanish!, Inishleigh!, Mannin!

498. *Dactylis glomerata* L.   Cock's-foot, Garbhfhéar

Common in lush grassland.

Sherkin!, Cape Clear!, Calfs!, Carthys!, Goat!, Long!, Castle!, Horse!, Skeams!, Heir!, Catalogues!, Sandy!, Quarantine!, Jeremy!, Spanish!, Inishleigh!, Mannin!

499. *Cynosurus cristatus* L.   Crested Dog's-tail, Coinfhéar

Abundant in drier grasslands.

Sherkin!, Cape Clear!, Calfs!, Long!, Castle!, Horse!, Skeams!, Heir!, Sandy!, Spanish!, Inishleigh!, Mannin!

500. *Catabrosa aquatica* (**L.**) **Beauv. var.** *litoralis* **Parn. (***C. aquatica* **subsp.** *minor* **(Bab.) Perring & P.D. Sell)**

Whorl-grass, Casfhéar uisce

Rare on upper part of strands, where streams flow from marshy ground to the sea.

Sherkin (Trabawn Strand, confirming record of Polunin 1949)!, Horse (W. end)!

A rare grass, this variety is known only from scattered stations in North and West Ireland and in Northern Britain (Perring & Sell 1968).

501. *Briza media* L.   Quaking-grass, Féar gortach

Rare in coastal grassland.

Sherkin (Silver Strand; near The Dock, KC 1992)!

502. *Glyceria declinata* **Breb.**   Small Sweet-grass, Milséan beag

Marshy ground.

Sherkin (as *G. maxima*, Polunin; LCW 1982), Cape Clear (near turbot farm)!, M Calf (LCW 1982), Long (BM & MWR 1995, confirming record of Polunin)!, Heir!

503. *Glyceria fluitans* (**L.**) **R.Br.**   Floating Sweet-grass, Milséan uisce

Pools and damp ground by slow streams.

Sherkin!, M & E Calf!, Long!, Castle!, Horse!, Skeam E!, Heir!, Spanish!

504. *Glyceria x pedicillata* **Towns. (***G. fluitans x plicata***)**

Hybrid Sweet-grass, Milseán hibrideach

Sherkin (near The Dock, HJL 1978).

Not previously recorded in Co. Cork; scattered and probably overlooked in Ireland.

505. *Bromus sterilis* L.   Sterile Brome, Brómas aimrid

Local on waysides.

Sherkin!, W Calf & Carthys (LCW 1982), Heir!

[**506.** *Bromus ramosus* **Huds.**   Hairy Brome, Brómas giobach

Sherkin (Polunin 1949).

Rare in South-West Ireland and probably extinct.]

[507. *Bromus commutatus* **Schrader**   **Meadow Brome, Brómas móinéir**

Cultivated land; probably extinct.

Sherkin (Polunin 1950).]

508. *Bromus hordeaceus* **L. subsp.** *hordeaceus*   **Soft Brome, Brómas bog**

Maritime grassland, occasionally on sand or shingle strands.

Sherkin!, Cape Clear!, E Calf!, Carthys (LCW 1982), Long!, Castle!, Horse!, Skeam E!, Heir!, Spanish!

509. *Bromus hordeaceus* **L. subsp.** *thominii* **(Hard.) Maire & Weiller (***B.thominii* **Hard.)**

                                      Soft Brome, Brómas bog

Rare on blown sand.

E Calf!

510. *Brachypodium sylvaticum* **(Huds.) Beauv.**   **False Brome, Brómas bréige**

Shady banks and the base of walls.

Sherkin!, Cape Clear!, Long!, Castle!, Horse!, Skeam E!, Heir!, Sandy!, Spanish!

511. *Elymus repens* **(L.) Gould**   **Common Couch, Broimfhéar**

Open, disturbed ground, especially at the top of shingle strands.

Sherkin!, Cape Clear! Calfs!, Long!, Castle (LCW 1982), Horse!, Skeams!, Heir!, Catalogues!, Spanish!, Mannin!

512. *Elymus farctus* **(Viv.) Runemark ex Melderis subsp.** *boreali-atlanticus* **(Simonet & Guinochet) Melderis**

                          Sand Couch, Broimfhéar gainimh

Upper part of strands and foredunes.

Sherkin (Silver Strand; Cow Strand; near Sherkin Point)!, E Calf (confirming record, as *Agropyron junceum*, of Allin 1883)!, Carthys!, Horse!, Heir!

513. *Elymus farctus x repens* **(***E. laxum* **(Fries) Tutin)**

Heir (S.E. end, BM 1995, confirming record of Polunin 1950)!

514. *Hordeum distichon* **L.**   **Two-rowed Barley, Eorna dhá shraith**

Rare on the borders of cultivated fields; a relic of former cultivation.

Heir (W. end, BM 1995)!

515. *Avena sativa* **L.**   **Oat, Coirce**

Cultivated ground, both as a crop and a relic of cultivation.

Sherkin!, Cape Clear!, W Calf!, Heir!

516. *Avenula pubescens* **(Huds.) Dumort.** **Downy Oat-grass, Coirce clumhach**

Coastal grassland; probably overlooked.

Cape Clear!, Heir!, Catalogues!, Sandy!

517. *Arrhenatherum elatius* **(L.) Beauv. ex J. & C. Presl subsp.** *bulbosus*

Onion Couch, Coirce bréige

Waysides and rank pastures.

Sherkin!, Cape Clear!, W & E Calf!, Carthys!, Long!, Castle!, Horse!, Skeams!, Heir!, Catalogues!, Sandy!, Quarantine!, Spanish!, Inishleigh!, Mannin!

This is the common variant of the species over much of Ireland and western Britain. The onion-like swellings of the lower stem internodes are a means of vegetative reproduction and the plant can be difficult to eradicate from cultivated land. Some plants (for example, from Sandy, BM 1995) are closer to subsp. *elatius*, which lacks the swellings.

518. *Koeleria macrantha* **(Ledeb.) Schultes** **Crested Hair-grass, Cailcfhéar**

Maritime grassland, especially over rock outcrops.

Sherkin!, Cape Clear!, Calfs!, Long!, Castle!, Horse!, Skeams!, Heir!, Catalogues!, Sandy!, Spanish!, Inishleigh!, Mannin!

519. *Trisetum flavescens* **(L.) Beauv.** **Yellow Oat-grass, Coirce buí**

Pastures above Trabawn, probably introduced with grass seed.

Sherkin (JRA & BM 1995)!

520. *Deschampsia cespitosa* **(L.) Beauv.** **Tufted Hair-grass, Móinfhéar garbh**

Cape Clear (Edmunds 1960).

521. *Aira praecox* **L.** **Early Hair-grass, Mionfhéar luath**

Open ground, especially on rock outcrops.

Sherkin!, Cape Clear!, Calfs!, Long!, Castle!, Horse!, Skeams!, Heir!, Catalogues!, Sandy!, Quarantine!, Jeremy!, Spanish!, Inishleigh!, Mannin!

522. *Aira caryophylla* **L.** **Silver Hair-grass, Mionfhéar geal**

Rocky and stony ground, walls and open grassland.

Sherkin!, Cape Clear!, Calfs!, Long!, Castle!, Horse!, Skeams!, Heir!, Catalogues!, Sandy!, Spanish!, Inishleigh!, Mannin!

Robust plants have been called subsp. *multiculmis* Dumort.

523. *Anthoxanthum odoratum* **L.** **Sweet Vernal-grass, Féar cumhra**

Ubiquitous in grassland.

Sherkin!, Cape Clear!, Calfs!, Goat!, Long!, Castle!, Horse!, Skeams!, Heir!, Catalogues!, Sandy!, Quarantine!, Jeremy!, Spanish!, Inishleigh!, Mannin!

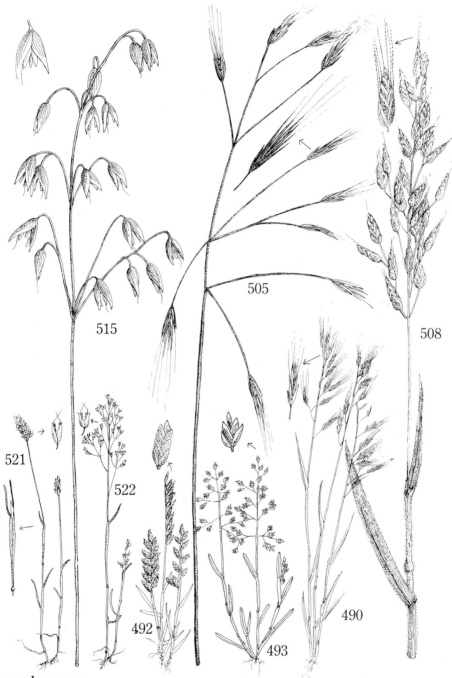

Annual grasses:

490 Squirreltail Brome   505 Sterile Brome   521 Early Hair-grass

492 Sea Fern-grass   508 Soft Brome   522 Silver Hair-grass

493 Annual Meadow-grass   515 Oat

524. *Holcus lanatus* L.   **Yorkshire-fog, Féar an chinn bháin**

Ubiquitous in grassland.

Sherkin!, Cape Clear!, Badger (NR 1993)!, Calfs!, Carthyṣ!, Goat!, Little Goat!, Long!, Castle!, Horse!, Skeams!, Heir!, Catalogues!, Sandy!, Quarantine!, Jeremy!, Spanish!, Inishleigh!, Mannin!

Records of Creeping Soft-grass from Cape Clear may refer to this species.

525. *Holcus mollis* L.   **Creeping Soft-grass, Mínfhéar reatha**

Rare in damp grassland.

Spanish (BM 1995)!

526. *Agrostis canina* L.   **Velvet Bent, Feorainn shlim**

Damp grassland.

Sherkin!, Cape Clear!, M Calf!, Long!, Horse!, Skeam W (LCW 1982), Skeam E!, Heir!, Catalogues!, Sandy!, Quarantine (LCW 1982), Jeremy!, Spanish!, Inishleigh!, Mannin!

527. *Agrostis vinealis* Schreber (*A. canina* L. subsp. *montana* Hartman) Hartman)

       Brown Bent, Feorainn dhonn

Dry grassland, giving it a reddish-brown tint in summer.

Sherkin!, Cape Clear!, Goat!, Calfs!, Long!, Castle!, Horse!, Skeams!, Heir!, Catalogues!, Sandy!, Spanish!, Inishleigh!, Mannin!

528. *Agrostis capillaris* L. (*A. tenuis* Sibth.)   **Common Bent, Feorainn mhín**

Dry grassland and heathland.

Sherkin!, Cape Clear!, Calfs!, Carthys (LCW 1982), Long!, Castle!, Horse!, Skeams!, Heir!, Catalogues!, Sandy!, Spanish!, Inishleigh!, Mannin!

529. *Agrostis gigantea* Roth   **Black Bent, Feorainn dhubh**

Occasional in disturbed grassland; probably under-recorded.

Sherkin!, Calfs (LCW 1982), Horse (Polunin 1950; LCW 1982), Sandy, Quarantine & Spanish (LCW 1982).

530. *Agrostis stolonifera* L.   **Creeping Bent, Feorainn**

Damp grassland, waysides and saltmarshes; common and variable.

Sherkin!, Cape Clear!, Badger!, Calfs!, Carthys!, Goat!, Long!, Castle!, Horse!, Skeams!, Heir!, Catalogues!, Sandy!, Quarantine!, Jeremy!, Spanish!, Inishleigh!, Mannin!

531. *Ammophila arenaria* (L.) Link   **Marram, Muiríneach**

Sand-dunes and areas of blown sand.

Sherkin (around Silver Strand and Cow Strand)!, E Calf!, Horse (W. end)!, Heir!

*532. *Phleum pratense* L.   **Timothy Grass, Tiomóid**

Grassland; probably introduced forage grass.

Cape Clear (Edmunds 1960).

533. *Alopecurus pratensis* L.   **Meadow Foxtail, Fiteog léana**

Waysides; perhaps introduced.

Sherkin!, W Calf (PCH & MWR 1994)!, Heir (KC 1992)!

A rather local grass in Western Ireland, first recorded in the islands only in 1992.

534. *Alopecurus geniculatus* L.   **Marsh Foxtail, Fiteog cham**

Damp grassland and disturbed ground.

Sherkin!, Cape Clear!, M & E Calf!, Long!, Castle!, Horse!, Skeams!, Heir!, Inishleigh!

535. *Parapholis strigosa* (Dumort.) C.E. Hubbard   **Sea Hard-grass, Cruafhéar**

Dry upper part of sandy salt-marsh.

Heir (JRA & NR 1993)!

Rare in Western Ireland and otherwise not recorded recently in Co. Cork.

536. *Phragmites australis* (Cav.) Trin. ex Steudel   **Common Reed, Giolcach**

Frequent and conspicuous in marshes, damp fields and margins of loughs and pools.

Sherkin!, Cape Clear!, E Calf!, Castle!, Horse!, Heir!, Spanish (LCW 1982).

537. *Danthonia decumbens* (L.) DC.   **Heath-grass, Féar caoráin**

Common in grassland and heathland.

Sherkin!, Cape Clear!, Calfs!, Long!, Castle!, Horse!, Skeams!, Heir!, Catalogues!, Sandy!, Jeremy!, Spanish!, Inishleigh!, Mannin!

538. *Molinia caerulea* (L.) Moench   **Purple Moor-grass, Fionnán**

Damp heaths and bogs.

Sherkin!, Cape Clear!, Calfs!, Goat!, Long!, Castle!, Horse!, Skeams!, Heir!, Catalogues!, Sandy!, Quarantine!, Jeremy!, Spanish!, Inishleigh!, Mannin!

ARACEAE - arum lilies

*539. *Zantedeschia aethiopica* (L.) Sprengel   **Easter Lily, Lile na Cásca**

Cultivated for ornament and sometimes escaping to walls, hedge-banks and waste ground.

Sherkin!, Cape Clear!, Long!, Heir!

LEMNACEAE - duckweeds

540. *Lemna minor* **L.**   **Duckweed, Ros lachan**

Pools, flooded ditches and wheel-ruts.

Sherkin!, Cape Clear!, M & E Calf!, Long!, Castle!, Horse!, Skeam E!, Heir!

SPARGANIACEAE - bur-reeds

541. *Sparganium erectum* **L.**   **Branched Bur-reed, Rísheisc**

Common in wet fields and marshes.

Sherkin!, Cape Clear!, Long!, Horse!, Heir!, Spanish!

All the plants from Sherkin, Cape Clear and Heir at least belong to subsp. *neglectum* (Beeby) Schinz & Thell., with pale brown, ellipsoidal fruits, gradually narrowed to a beak.

542. *Sparganium angustifolium* **Michaux (*S. emersum* (Rehman)**

Floating Bur-reed, Rísheisc chaol

Peaty pools and loughs.

Sherkin (Lough Ordree)!, Long (E. end, PCH & MWR 1994)!

543. *Sparganium minimum* **Wallr.**   **Least Bur-reed, Rísheisc mhion**

Cape Clear (RAP, Polunin 1950, Richards 1968).

Also recorded from Three Castles Head (RAP). It is scattered in Ireland, mostly in the west.

TYPHACEAE - bulrushes

544. *Typha latifolia* **L.**   **Bulrush, Coigeal na mban sí**

Rare in wet marshes and margins of loughs.

Sherkin (Tramore and Lough Ordree)!

CYPERACEAE - clubrushes, spike-rushes and sedges

These plants form a major element of grassland, wet places and bogs. Sedges are often mistaken for grasses, from which they can mostly be separated by their stems, which are triangular in section. At least 23 sedges occur in Roaringwater Bay.

545. *Scirpus maritimus* **L. (*Bolboschoenus maritimus* (L.) Palla)**

Sea Club-rush, Bogshifín mara

Pool-margins by the sea.

Sherkin!, Calfs!, Heir!, Spanish!, Inishleigh!, Mannin!

546. *Scirpus lacustris* **L. subsp.** *lacustris* (*Schoenoplectus lacustris* (L.) **Palla**)

Common Club-rush, Bogshifín

Margins of loughs.

Sherkin (Lough Ordree)!

547. *Scirpus lacustris* **L. subsp.** *tabernaemontani* **C.C. Gmelin** (*Schoenoplectus tabernaemontani* (C.C. Gmelin) **Palla**)

Grey Club-rush, Bogshifín liath

Margins of brackish loughs and pools; brackish marshes.

Sherkin!, Cape Clear!, Calfs!, Horse!, Skeam E!, Heir!, Mannin!

548. *Scirpus setaceus* **L.** (*Isolepis setacea* (L.) **R.Br.**)

Bristle Club-rush, Crualuachair bhiorach

Wet ground.

Sherkin!, Cape Clear!, M & E Calf!, Long!, Castle!, Horse!, Skeam E!, Heir!, Inishleigh!

549. *Scirpus cernuus* **Vahl** (*Isolepis cernua* (Vahl) **Roemer & Schultes**)

Slender Club-rush, Crualuachair chaol

Wet ground, often near the sea.

Sherkin!, Cape Clear!, W & M Calf!, Long!, Castle!, Horse!, Skeam E!, Heir!, Spanish!

550. *Scirpus fluitans* **L.** (*Eleogiton fluitans* (L.) **Link**)

Floating Club-rush, Brobh ar snámh

Peaty pools.

Sherkin!, Cape Clear!, M & E Calf!, Long!, Heir!, Spanish!, Inishleigh!

551. *Scirpus caespitosus* **L.** (*Trichophorum caespitosum* (L.) **Hartman**)

Deergrass, Cíb cheanngheal

Cape Clear (Edmunds 1960).

552. *Eriophorum angustifolium* **Honckeny**   **Common Cottongrass, Ceannbhán**

Local in boggy places.

Sherkin (north side of Lough Ordree)!, Cape Clear!, Long!, Sandy!, Spanish!

553. *Eriophorum vaginatum* **L.**   **Hare's-tail Cottongrass, Ceannbhán gaelach**

Rare in boggy places.

Cape Clear (Edmunds 1960).

554. *Eleocharis palustris* (**L.**) **Roemer & Schultes**   **Common Spike-rush, Cíb dhéise**

Damp ground and margins of pools.

Sherkin!, Cape Clear!, Calfs!, Long!, Castle!, Horse!, Skeams!, Heir!, Spanish!

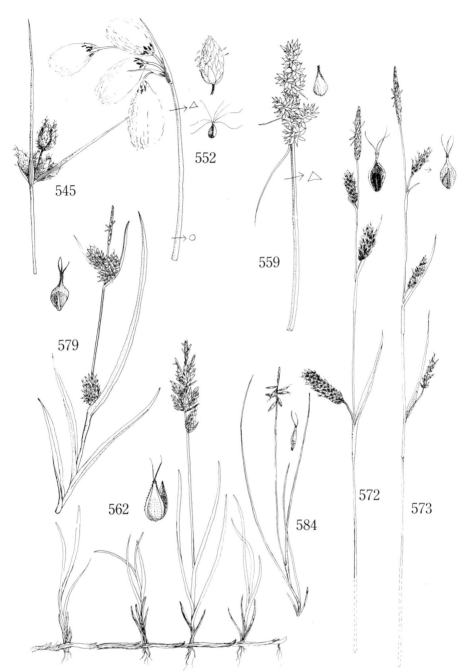

Sedges and their allies:

545 Sea Club-rush

552 Common Cottongrass

559 False Fox-sedge

562 Sand Sedge

572 Green-ribbed Sedge

573 Distant Sedge

579 Common Yellow-Sedge

584 Flea Sedge

555. *Eleocharis uniglumis* (Link) Schultes   Slender Spike-rush, Spícíneach chaol

Damp, brackish grassland near the sea.

Sherkin (Sherkin Point; BM 1995, confirming record of Polunin 1950)!, Calfs!, Heir (NR 1993)!

556. *Eleocharis multicaulis* (Sm.) Desv.

Many-stalked Spike-rush, Spícíneach thortógach

Boggy places.

Sherkin!, Cape Clear (Richards 1969, LCW 1982), Calfs!, Long!, Horse!, Heir!, Sandy!, Spanish!

557. *Schoenus nigricans* L.   Black Bog-rush, Sifín

Local in bogs.

Sherkin (S.W. end of island)!, Cape Clear!, Long!

558. *Carex paniculata* L.   Greater Tussock-sedge, Cíb thortógach

Reedswamp.

Sherkin (Lough Ordree; BM 1995, confirming record of Polunin 1950)!, Cape Clear (Sharrock 1965).

559. *Carex otrubae* Podp.   False Fox-sedge, Cíb an mhadra rua

Damp, grassy places.

Sherkin!, Cape Clear!, Calfs!, Long!, Castle!, Horse!, Skeam E!, Heir!, Sandy!, Spanish!, Inishleigh!, Mannin!

Rather local and mainly coastal in Ireland.

560. *Carex muricata* L. subsp. *lamprocarpa* Celak.

Small-fruited Prickly-sedge, Cíb dheilgneach

Heathy banks and walls.

Sherkin (near Murphy's Bar, Abbey and just north of The Cross; confirming records of Allin 1883, Polunin, T O'M 1976)!, Cape Clear (South Harbour, O'Mahony 1994), Long!

Rather widespread in Mid Cork, but the stations in Roaringwater Bay are, with two others, the only ones in West Cork (O'Mahony 1986 & pers. comm., Wyse Jackson 1995). Otherwise not common in Ireland, mainly in the south-east. Subsp. *muricata* does not occur in Ireland.

561. *Carex divulsa* Stokes subsp. *divulsa*   Grey Sedge, Cíb liath

Damp, shady places.

Sherkin!, Cape Clear!, Long!, Heir!, Spanish!

Local in Ireland; mainly near southern and eastern coasts.

562. *Carex arenaria* L.   Sand Sedge, Cíb ghainimh

Locally common on blown sand.

Sherkin (Silver Strand; Cow Strand; O'Connor's beach)!, E Calf!, Long!, Horse!, Heir!, Sandy!

563. *Carex remota* **L.**   **Remote Sedge, Cíb scartha**

Rare in damp shady places.

Sherkin (Trabawn, OP, unpublished notes), Long (NR 1993; main settlement, BM & MWR 1995)!

564. *Carex ovalis* **Good.**   **Oval Sedge, Cíb mhaol**

Damp ground.

Sherkin!, Cape Clear!, M & E Calf!, Long!, Castle!, Horse!, Skeam E!, Heir!, Catalogues!, Sandy!, Spanish!, Inishleigh!, Mannin!

565. *Carex echinata* **Murray**   **Star Sedge, Cíb na réaltaí**

Marshes.

Sherkin!, Cape Clear!, Long!, Heir!, Spanish!, Mannin (LCW 1982).

566. *Carex lasiocarpa* **Ehrh.**   **Slender Sedge, Cíb chaol**

Pools in bogs.

Cape Clear (lough near O'Driscoll Castle, JRA & NR 1993)!, Long!

Scarce in the southernmost Irish counties; more a plant of the Midlands and Connemara.

567. *Carex riparia* **Curtis.**   **Greater Pond-sedge, Cíb locháin mhór**

Rare on lake margins.

Sherkin (Lough Ordree, BM 1995)!

Mostly confined to the south and east of Ireland. This is the first post-1950 record from West Cork.

568. *Carex pseudocyperus* **L.**   **Cyperus Sedge, Cíb sheisceach**

Rare in wet marshes.

Sherkin (Tramore and Lough Ordree, PCH & MWR 1994, BM 1995, confirming record of Polunin 1950)!

The two small populations on Sherkin are an outlier of this local Irish sedge, which occurs mostly in the Midlands. Polunin (unpublished notes) also recorded it in the marsh at Trabawn. The only other extant Munster records are from swamp woodland on Ross Island, Killarney, Kerry (Kelly 1985), and a marsh at Curragh Chase, Co. Limerick (Reynolds 1988).

569. *Carex rostrata* **Stokes**   **Bottle Sedge, Cíb ghobach**

Margin of pools.

Sherkin (Lough Ordree; N.E. corner of island, KC 1992)!, Spanish (NR 1993)!

570. *Carex flacca* Schreber　　　　　　　　Glaucous Sedge, Cíb liathghorm

Damp heaths.

Sherkin!, Cape Clear!, Calfs!, Long!, Castle!, Skeams!, Heir!, Catalogues!, Sandy!, Spanish!, Inishleigh!

571. *Carex panicea* L.　　　　　　　　Carnation Sedge, Cíb chruithneachta

Wet, heathy ground.

Sherkin!, Cape Clear!, Calfs!, Goat!, Long!, Castle!, Horse!, Skeams!, Heir!, Catalogues!, Sandy!, Spanish!, Inishleigh!

572. *Carex binervis* Sm.　　　　　　　　Green-ribbed Sedge, Cíb fhéithghlas

Common in heathland, often by the sea.

Sherkin!, Cape Clear!, Calfs!, Goat!, Long!, Castle!, Horse!, Skeams!, Heir!, Catalogues!, Sandy!, Jeremy!, Spanish!, Inishleigh!, Mannin!

573. *Carex distans* L.　　　　　　　　Distant Sedge, Cíb scrogallach

Locally common on damp, rocky ground by the sea.

Sherkin!, Cape Clear!, Calfs!, Long!, Castle!, Horse!, Skeams!, Heir!, Catalogues!, Sandy!, Spanish!

574. *Carex punctata* Gaud.　　　　　　　　Dotted Sedge, Cíb bhallach

Rare on damp cliffs, slopes and rocky ground by the sea.

Sherkin (Horseshoe Harbour)!, Cape Clear (also reported by O'Mahony 1994)!, Horse (Polunin 1950, RF 1993, MWR 1994)!, Skeam E!, Spanish (NR 1993)!

Some 20 or so stations are known for this rather scarce coastal sedge in West Cork, but all the populations are small (David 1981). It was recorded from Toe Head by Allin (1883). Munster and Connemara are its Irish headquarters.

This attractive plant occurs in similar places to Distant Sedge, which it resembles closely. Dotted Sedge is the more erect of the two, with slightly broader, more yellow leaves, longer bracts (that exceed the inflorescence) and fruits orientated at a right angle to the stem axis (not obliquely angled).

575. *Carex extensa* Good.　　　　　　　　Long-bracted Sedge, Cíb fhada

Margins of rocky pools by the sea.

Sherkin!, Cape Clear!, Calfs!, Long!, Castle!, Horse!, Skeams!, Heir!, Catalogues!, Sandy!, Spanish!, Inishleigh!, Mannin!

576. *Carex hostiana* DC.　　　　　　　　Tawny Sedge, Cíb odhar

Damp ground near the sea.

Sherkin (Tramore)!, Skeam E!

577. *Carex hostiana x viridula* (*C. x fulva* Gooden., *C. x appeliana* Zahn.)

Marshy ground near the sea.

Sandy (BM 1995)!

A specimen from Sandy was identified by A.O. Chater, who noted: "subsp. *oedocarpa* probably the subspecies involved. The utricles [fruits] are almost empty."

578. *Carex viridula* Michaux subsp. *brachyrrhyncha* (Celak.) B. Schmidt (*C. lepidocarpa* Tausch., *C. marshallii* A. Bennett)

Long-stalked Yellow-sedge, Cíb bhuí chosach

Rare in damp grassland by the sea.

Sherkin (LCW 1982), M Calf!, Castle (LCW 1982), Sandy (LCW 1982).

This is more characteristically a plant of base-rich fens in the Midlands and elsewhere. Other records of this sedge from Roaringwater Bay probably refer to Common Yellow-sedge.

579. *Carex viridula* Michaux subsp. *oedocarpa* (Andersson) B. Schmidt (*C. demissa* Hornem., *C. tumidocarpa* Andersson)

Common Yellow-sedge, Cíb bhuí mhóna

Widespread in damp heathland, often near the sea.

Sherkin!, Cape Clear!, Calfs!, Long!, Castle!, Horse!, Skeams!, Heir!, Catalogues!, Sandy!, Spanish!, Mannin!

580. *Carex viridula* Michaux subsp. *viridula* (*C. serotina* Mérat)

Small-fruited Yellow-sedge, Cíb bhuí bheag

Damp heathland; mostly at the landward side of saltmarshes.

Sherkin!, Cape Clear!, Long!, Horse!, Heir!, Sandy!, Spanish!

Commenting on a specimen, A.O. Chater noted that the "small size of the utricle [fruit] and comparative abruptness of [its] beak suggests subsp. *viridula*". Other records of this plant from Roaringwater Bay are probably based on small individuals of Common Yellow-sedge.

581. *Carex caryophyllea* Latourr.   **Spring Sedge, Cíb earraigh**

Cape Clear (Sharrock 1965), Horse (RF 1993), Skeam E!

582. *Carex pilulifera* L.   **Pill Sedge, Cíb na bpaidríní**

Heaths and rocky ground.

Sherkin (above Lough Ordree, BM 1995)!, Cape Clear (South Harbour, JRA & NR 1993, confirming record of Richards 1969)!, M Calf (TO'M 1992, NR 1993)!

Although it is widespread in Ireland, there are few records of this sedge from Co. Cork.

583. *Carex nigra* (L.) Reichard   **Common Sedge, Cíb dhubh**

The common sedge of damp grassland; also in and around pools.

Sherkin!, Cape Clear!, Calfs!, Goat!, Long!, Castle!, Horse!, Skeam W (LCW 1982), Skeam E!, Heir!, Catalogues!, Sandy!, Jeremy!, Spanish!, Inishleigh!, Mannin!

A record of Water Sedge (*C. aquatilis* Wahlenb.) from Cape Clear requires confirmation; its other Irish stations are mostly in the Midlands and Ulster. Variants of Common Sedge can resemble it closely (C.D. Preston, pers. comm.).

584. *Carex pulicaris* **L.**   **Flea Sedge, Cíb na ndreancaidí**

Damp heathland.

Sherkin!, Cape Clear!, M Calf!, Long!, Heir!, Sandy!, Spanish!

ORCHIDACEAE – orchids

These attractive flowers have a characteristic 'lip' and are massed in spikes. More work is needed on the spotted- and marsh-orchids of the islands, notoriously difficult to separate in Western Ireland.

585. *Spiranthes spiralis* **(L.) Chevall.**   **Autumn Lady's-tresses, Cúilín Muire**

Widespread but local in short, coastal grassland, often around rock-outcrops. Flowering August to September.

Sherkin (confirming records of Allin 1883, Polunin 1949)!, Cape Clear!, E Calf!, Long!, Horse!, Skeam E!, Heir!

First recorded by Allin (1883); rather common on the coast of West Cork.

586. *Dactylorhiza incarnata* **(L.) Soó**   **Early Marsh-orchid, Magairlín mór**

Damp grassland.

Sherkin!, Cape Clear (Sharrock 1965), W & E Calf!, Long!, Horse!, Heir!, Catalogues!, Sandy!, Spanish!

587. *Dactylorhiza majalis* **(Reichenb.) P. Hunt & Summerh. subsp.** *occidentalis* **(Pugsley) P.D. Sell**

                      Western Marsh-orchid, Magairlín gaelach

Damp grassland; flowering May to late June.

Sherkin!, Cape Clear!, Calfs!, Long!, Castle!, Horse!, Skeam E!, Heir!, Sandy!, Quarantine!, Spanish!

Restricted to Ireland and the Outer Hebrides. Known locally as the 'West Cork Orchid', this handsome, early-flowering orchid, with violet-purple flowers, is widespread in Western Ireland.

588. *Dactylorhiza majalis* **(Reichenb.) P. Hunt & Summerh. subsp.** *purpurella* **(Stephenson & T.A. Stephenson) David Moore & Soó (***Dactylorhiza purpurella* **(Stephenson & T.A. Stephenson) Soó)**

                      Northern Marsh-orchid, Magairlín corcra

Sherkin (E. of Sherkin Point, NS 1992).

This orchid, with purple or reddish-purple flowers and flowering slightly later than Western Marsh-orchid, has been treated by some authors as a distinct species.

589. *Dactylorhiza maculata* **(L.) Soó subsp.** *ericetorum* **(Linton) P. Hunt & Summerh.**

                      Heath Spotted-orchid, Na circíní

Locally common on heaths and grassy banks.

Sherkin!, Cape Clear!, W Calf!, Long!, Horse!, Heir!, Catalogues!, Spanish!

Records of Common Spotted-orchid (*D. fuchsii* (Druce) Soó), a plant of lime-rich soils, from Sherkin probably refer to this plant.

590. *Anacamptis pyramidalis* **(L.) L.C.M. Richard**

Pyramidal Orchid, Magairlín na stuaice

Rare in lime-rich grassland on stable blown sand.

Sherkin (near Cow Strand)!

Very rare in West Cork, this orchid also grows at Barley Cove on the mainland (Wyse Jackson 1995).

A Sherkin record of another orchid, Common Twayblade (*Listera ovata* (L.) R.Br.), requires confirmation.

CHAROPHYTES: stoneworts (Nos 591-592)

A small group of green algae of complex structure, found in fresh and brackish waters, that require clean, usually lime-rich, water and are sensitive to pollution. Traditionally included in 19th century Floras as honorary 'Higher Plants', the last decade has seen a revival of interest in stoneworts.

591. *Chara hispida* **L.**

Loughs and pools.

Sherkin (Trabawn, OP, unpublished notes; Lough Ordree)!, Cape Clear (East Bog)!, Long!, Heir!

Generally common in western Ireland, although Polunin was the first to report it from West Cork (plant record in *Watsonia*, 1: 263, 1950).

592. *Nitella translucens* **Agardh.**

Sherkin (Lough Ordree, "dominant on floor of lake", OP, unpublished notes; NS 1992), Cape Clear (OP, unpublished notes).

Described by Phillips as frequent in the south of West Cork (Praeger 1901).

REFERENCES

Akeroyd, J.R. (1983) Further notes on *Trifolium occidentale* D.E. Coombe in Ireland. *Irish Naturalists Journal*, 21: 32-34.

Akeroyd, J.R. (1986) Oleg Vladimirovich Polunin (1914-1985). *Watsonia*, 16: 105-107.

Akeroyd, J.R. (1993) *Rumex pulcher* L. in Ireland. *Irish Naturalists Journal*, 24: 284-285.

Akeroyd, J.R. & Clarke, K. (1993) *Dianthus armeria* L. new to Ireland and other rare plants in West Cork. *Watsonia*, 19: 185-187.

Akeroyd, J.R. & Doogue, D. (1988) *Plantago major* L. subsp. *intermedia* (DC.) Arcangeli in Ireland. *Irish Naturalists Journal*, 22: 441-443.

Allen, D.E. (1950) Plant notes. *Anagallis arvensis* L. *Proceedings of the Botanical Society of the British Isles*, 1: 156-157.

Allin, T. (1883) *The flowering plants and ferns of the County Cork.* Weston-super-Mare.

Baker, H.G. (1948) Stages in invasion and replacement demonstrated by species of *Melandrium [Silene]. Journal of Ecology*, 36: 96-110.

Brodie, J. & Sheehy Skeffington, M. (1990) Inishbofin: a resurvey of the flora. *Irish Naturalists Journal*, 23: 293-298.

Clayton, G., Graham, J.R., Higgs, K., Holland, C.H. & Naylor, D. (1980) Devonian rocks in Ireland: a review. *Journal of Earth Sciences, Royal Dublin Society*, 2: 161-183.

Colgan, N. & Scully (1898) *Cybele Hibernica.* 2nd ed. Hodges, Figgis & Co., Dublin.

Conroy, D. & Monaghan, D. (1975) *Lotus subbiflorus* Lag. on Sherkin Island, Co. Cork. *Irish Naturalists Journal*, 18: 254.

Conry, M. & Ryan, P. (1962) Soils, in *West Cork Resource Survey*, pp. A15-A43. An Foras Taluntas, Dublin.

Cotton, D.C.F. & Cowley, M. (1993) New records of vascular plants from Co. Sligo (H28) and Leitrim (H29). *Irish Naturalists Journal*, 24: 288-295.

Curran, P.L. (1985) *Montia fontana* L. subsp. *chondrosperma* (Fenzl) Walters on cultivated bog. *Irish Naturalists Journal*, 21: 446-448.

Curtis, T.G.F. & Harrington, T.J. (1987) A second station for *Ranunculus tripartitus* DC. in Kerry (H1). *Irish Naturalists Journal*, 22: 204-205.

Curtis, T.G.F. & McGough, H.N. (1988) *The Irish Red Data Books. 1. Vascular Plants.* Stationery Office, Dublin.

Curtis, T.G.F., McGough, H.N. & Wymer, E.D. (1988) The discovery and ecology of rare and threatened arable weeds, previously considered extinct in Ireland, on the Aran Islands, Co. Galway. *Irish Naturalists Journal*, 22: 505-512.

David, R.W. (1981) The distribution of *Carex punctata* Gaud. in Britain, Ireland and Isle of Man. *Watsonia*, 13: 318-321.

Day, J.P. & Copinger, W.A. (eds) (1893) *The ancient and present state of the County and City of Cork. By Charles Smith, M.D.*, Cork Historical and Archaeological Society, Cork.

Doyle, G.T. & Foss, P.J. (1986) A resurvey of the Clare Island flora. *Irish Naturalists Journal*, 22: 85-89.

Edmunds, M. (1960) Plants found on Cape Clear Island during 1960. *Cape Clear Bird Observatory Rep.*, 2: 27-29.

Fahy, E. (1975) *Ornithopus perpusillus* L. on Sherkin Island. *Irish Naturalists Journal*, 18: 254.

FitzGerald, R. (1993) The discovery of *Lotus subbiflorus* Lag. in south-east Ireland. *Irish Naturalists Journal*, 25: 240-242.

Graham, J.R. & Reilly, T.A. (1972) The Sherkin Formation (Devonian) of south-west County Cork. *Bulletin of the Geological Survey of Ireland*, 1: 281-300.

Hart, H.C. (1898) *Flora of the County Donegal.* Sealy, Bryers & Walker, Dublin.

Hawes, P.T.J. (1993) *Orchis morio* L. at Barley cove, Co. Cork. *Irish Naturalists Journal*, 24: 222.

Howes, E.A. (1993) Some comments on the genus *Parietaria*. *BSBI Welsh Bulletin*, no.55: 15-18.

Hudson, H.J. (1975) Plant notes from some Irish counties. *Irish Naturalists Journal*, 18: 222-223.

Jalas, J. & Suominen, J. (1986) *Atlas Florae Europaeae*, 7. Societas Biologica Fennica Vanamo, Helsinki.

Kelly, D.L. (1985) Plant records from about Ireland, 1965-1983. *Irish Naturalists Journal*, 21: 416-419.

Kelly, D.L. & Doogue, D. (1990) New records for hybrid docks. *Irish Naturalists Journal*, 23: 218-219.

Lennon, H.J. (1981) Post-Glacial vegetational history of Sherkin Island, West Cork. *Journal of Sherkin Island*, 1(2): 1-12.

Lewis, S. (1937) *A topographical history of Ireland* (2 vols). S. Lewis & Co., London.

Lucas, A.T. (1960) *Furze. A survey and history of its uses in Ireland.* National Museum of Ireland, Dublin.

McCracken, E. (1971) *The Irish woods since Tudor times.* David & Charles, Newton Abbot.

McGough, H.N. (1988) Additions to and notes on the flora of Clare (H9), Galway (H15-17), Longford (H24) and Leitrim (H29). *Irish Naturalists Journal*, 22: 411-413.

Mitchell, F. (1986) *The Shell Guide to Reading the Irish Landscape.* Country House, Dublin.

Mogford, D.J. (1974) Flower colour polymorphism in *Cirsium palustre*. 1. *Heredity*, 33: 241-256.

O'Brien, W. (1994) Bronze Age copper mining on Mount Gabriel. *Mizen Journal*, 2: 27-32.

O'Donovan, J.E. (1953) *Lotus hispidus* and *Trigonella ornithopodioides* in West Cork. *Irish Naturalists Journal*, 11: 108-109.

O'Donovan, J.E. & O'Regan, B. (1952) Notes on some native and alien plants in W. Cork. *Irish Naturalists Journal*, 10: 235-238.

O'Mahony, T. (1975) First county and vice-county records for county Cork plants. *Irish Naturalists Journal*, 18: 238-241.

O'Mahony, T. (1979) *Inula crithmoides* L. and *Trifolium striatum* L. in the Cork flora. *Bulletin of the Irish Biogeographical Society*, 3: 7-10.

O'Mahony, T. (1985) The history of *Geranium purpureum* Vill. in the Irish flora. *Irish Naturalists Journal*, 21: 517-521.

O'Mahony, T, (1986) *Carex muricata* L. subsp. *lamprocarpa* Celak. in the Cork flora: some recent records and autecological observations. *Irish Naturalists Journal*, 22: 23-25.

O'Mahony,T. (1992) A report on the flora of Cork (v.cc. H3-H5), 1991. *Irish Botanical News*, 2: 26-28.

O'Mahony,T. (1993) A report on the flora of Cork (v.cc. H3-H5), 1992. *Irish Botanical News*, 3: 32-34.

O'Mahony,T. (1994) A report on the flora of Cork (v.cc. H3-H5), 1993. *Irish Botanical News*, 4: 17-19.

O'Mahony,T. (1995) A report on the flora of Cork (v.cc. H3-H5), 1994. *Irish Botanical News*, 5: 12-15.

O'Regan, J. (1994) Memories of life on the island of West Skeam. *Mizen Journal*, 2: 8-19.

O'Reilly, D. (1994) *Sherkin Island*. Sliabh Mór Press, Sherkin, Co. Cork.

O'Sullivan, A.M. (1979a) Occurrence of *Datura stramonium* L. and other aliens in Irish tillage fields. *Irish Naturalists Journal*, 19: 434-435.

O'Sullivan, A.M. (1979b) Watch for it - it is dangerous. *BIATAS - The Tillage Farmer*, 33: 93-95.

Palmer, H. (1986) Rainfall of Sherkin Island 1973-1984. *Bulletin of Sherkin Island*, No. 5.

Palmer, H. (1995a) Sunshine Records of Sherkin Island 1974-1984. *Bulletin of Sherkin Island*, No. 10.

Palmer, H. (1995b) Air Temperatures of Sherkin Island 1975-1984. *Bulletin of Sherkin Island*, No. 11.

Perring, F.H. & Sell, P.D., eds (1968) *Critical supplement to the Atlas of the British Flora*, Thomas Nelson & Son, London.

Perring, F.H. & Walters, S.M. (1976) *Atlas of the British Flora*. 2nd ed. EP Publishing, Wakefield.

Polunin, O. (1949) Draft typescript of Polunin (1950), held at Sherkin Island Marine Station, with letter from *Watsonia* editor E.F. Warburg. Reproduced in Appendix 1.

Polunin, O. (1950) Notes and additions to the flora of the islands of S.W. Cork. *Watsonia*, 1: 359-363.

Power, T. (1845) The Botanist's guide for the county of Cork. In *contributions towards a Fauna and Flora of the County of Cork*. [British Association meeting, Cork, 1843] Cuverian Society of Cork, London & Cork.

Praeger, R, Ll. (1901) *Irish Topographic Botany*. Royal Irish Academy, Dublin.

Praeger, R. Ll. (1911) Clare Island Survey. Part 10. Phanerogama and Pteridophyta. *Proceedings of the Royal Irish Academy*, 31: 1-112.

Praeger, R. Ll. (1934) *The botanist in Ireland*. Hodges, Figgis & Co., Dublin.

Praeger, R. Ll. (1936) *The way that I went*. Hodges, Figgis & Co., Dublin.

Proctor, M.C.F. (1962) The British forms of *Tuberaria guttata* (L.) Fourreau. *Watsonia*, 5: 236-250.

Reynolds, S. (1988) Plant records from Co. Limerick (H8). *Irish Naturalists Journal*, 22: 533-534.

Rich, T.C.G. & Rich, M.B.D. (1988) *Plant crib*. BSBI, London.

Richards, A.J. (1969) Some 1951 plant records from Cape Clear Island. *Cape Clear Bird Observatory Report*, 10: 32.

Richards, A.J. (1973) Higher Plants. In Sharrock, J.T.R. (ed.) *The natural history of Cape Clear Island*. T. & A.D. Poyser.

Scannell, M.J.P. & Synnott, D.M. (1987) *Census catalogue of the flora of Ireland*. 2nd ed. Stationery Office, Dublin.

Scully, R.W. (1916) *Flora of the County Kerry.* Hodges, Figgis & Co., Dublin.

Sharrock, J.T. R. (1961) Plants found on Cape Clear Island. *Cape Clear Bird Observatory Report*, 3: 17.

Sharrock, J.T.R. (1962) Plants found on Cape Clear Island. *Cape Clear Bird Observatory Report*, 4: 31.

Sharrock, J.T.R. (1967) Additions and corrections to the Cape Clear Island plant list. *Cape Clear Bird Observatory Rep.*, 7: 50-51.

Stace, C.A. (1991) *New Flora of the British Isles.* Cambridge University Press, Cambridge.

Stearn, W.T. (1978) European species of *Allium* and allied genera of Alliaceae: a synonymic revision. *Annales Musei Goulandris*, 4: 83-198.

Synnott, D.M. (1979) Folk-lore, legend and Irish plants. In Nelson, E.C. & Brady, A., eds, *Irish gardening and horticulture*, pp.36-43. R.H.S. Ireland, Dublin.

Thompson, P.A. (1973) Effects of cultivation on the germination character of the Corn Cockle (*Agrostemma githago* L.). *Annals of Botany* 37: 133-154.

Webb, D.A. (1952) The flora and vegetation of Ireland. *Veroff. d. Geobotanischen Institutes Rübel, Zürich*, 25: 17-49.

Webb, D.A. (1957) Botany. 1 Vegetation and flora. In *A view of Ireland* , pp. 40-58. British Association for the Advancement of Science, Dublin.

Webb, D.A. & Scannell, M.J.P. (1983) *Flora of Connemara and The Burren.* Royal Dublin Society and Cambridge University Press, Cambridge.

Wells, T.C.E. (1967) *Dianthus armeria* L. at Woodwalton Fen, Hunts. *Proceedings of the Botanical Society of the British Isles*, 6: 337-342.

White, J., ed. (1982) *Studies on Irish Vegetation*. Royal Dublin Society, Dublin.

Wyse Jackson, M.B. (1995) Annotated records for rare, critical or under-recorded vascular plant taxa from Ireland. *Irish Naturalists Journal*, 25: 44-57.

APPENDIX 1. Unpublished manuscript of Oleg Polunin (1949)

The original ms., together with other papers relating to Oleg Polunin's work on Sherkin Island, is in the library of Sherkin Island Marine Station.

<u>The Flora of Sherkin Island S.W. Cork</u>

A visit to Sherkin Island during August 1947 revealed an interesting collection of flowering plants, and several new vice-county records were made. S.W. Cork has received little attention from botanists, & so far as I am aware no previous list has been published of plants of this island. The list is not complete but I propose to set it down here in case I have no opportunity of returning.

Mr R.D. Meikle is in possession of the copy of T. Allin's "The Flowering Plants & Ferns of the County Cork" 1883, which belonged to R.A. Phillips. Phillips's own additions to the Cork Flora are inserted in this copy in his own handwriting. Mr Meikle and I have checked this annotated copy & all Sherkin Island localities given by Phillips have been added to my list. Phillips is the only botanist to have worked this area with any degree of thoroughness. Most of his records were made between the years 1896-1902 & he did little collecting during the latter part of his life.

Sherkin Island lies off the coast of S.W. Cork and with Clear Island and the Fastnet Rock forms the southern-most group of islands of Ireland. These islands are the summits of what was once a range of mountains formed of Old Red Sandstone. Subsequent subsidence and erosion of the valleys has isolated these areas. Sherkin I. is about 3 miles long & from 1/2-1 mile in width. A rib of high ground, which rises to 300 ft, runs down the whole length of the southern coast. This forms a wild exposed rocky coastline. To the north of this ridge of high ground there are a series of low ridges forming a highly indented and varied coast of beautiful white sandy bays, min[i]ature salt marshes, dunes and pebble beaches. There are occasional small lakes separated from the sea by sand bars, & lakelets among the rocks which are subjected to sea spray. This interesting collection of habitats were [sic] found to be rich in species and would certainly repay further study.

The soils are characteristically acid and develop a mixed "heath" vegetation dominated by Ulex [Gorse], Erica, Calluna [heathers] & pteridium [Bracken]. Molinietum [vegetation dominated by Purple Moor-grass] & Juncetum [rushes] develop in wetter localities. There are no woodlands and consequently some common or characteristic woodland species are absent. Calcareous sand is regularly dug from the bays and spread over the pastures & cultivated land. This encourages the development of a rich and probably neutral grassland.

Approximately 1/4 of the island is cultivated. The flatter ground lying between the rocky heath-covered ridges generally carries a few acres of wheat or oats. Potato gradens, rich in arable weeds, & small areas of pastures for hay and fattening also lie in these areas and along the sheltered north & east coasts. There are about 50 smallholdings each with a dozen or so cattle, a horse or two & some chickens. The cattle graze over the whole of the island but there are some unfrequented and inaccessible areas. The small fields are separated by dilapidated stone walls often covered with an impenetrable tange of Lonicera [Honeysuckle], Pteridium [Bracken] & Rubi [Brambles]. The rough lanes have a rich flora along their margins which contrasts markedly with that of the mainland roads with their faster moving traffic. There are no Sheep, Goats or Rabbits on the island. The absence of Rabbits is striking as they abound on the mainland and Clear Island; the inhabitants say they will not live on the island - "they sicken and die after two months because there is a poisonous weed". It would obviously be very interesting to acertain whether there is any truth in this statement.

R.Ll. Praeger's census list in his "The Botanist in Ireland" 1934 lists 726 species for S.W. Cork vice-county H.3 [i.e. West Cork]. On Sherkin Island I listed 335 species in August 1947. It is interesting to note that <u>Eryngium campestre</u> [Field Eryngo] which Praeger says "grows freely on Sherkin Island, and is looked on by R.A. Phillips as possibly native" — was not seen by me in 1947.

The island lies well to the south of the areas of W. Ireland where the Irish-Lusitanian [West European] species have their headquarters. <u>Euphorbia hyberna</u> [Irish Spurge] which is frequent on the Island is the exception. <u>Cicendia filiformis</u> [Yellow Centaury] is practically at its northern limit here.

A visit at an earlier date & closer attention to critical genera & the Gramineae [grasses] in particular would most certainly reveal additions to this list.

I should like to thank Mr N.Y. Sandwith [Noel Yvri Sandwith (1901-1965), noted botanist and classical scholar] and Mr R.D. Meikle [Desmond Meikle, willow specialist acknowledged in the present Flora] for their help and encouragement; they have named & confirmed many of the plants for me. Mr C.E. Hubbard [Charles Edward Hubbard (1900-1980), internationally renowned grass specialist], Mr E. Nelmes [Ernest Nelmes (1895-59), sedge specialist], and Mr G.M. Ash [Gerald Mortimer Ash (1900-1959), willowherb specialist] have kindly named many of the grasses, sedges and willow-herbs.

Ranunculus baudotii Godr. In two small lakelets by the sea on Sherkin Point & S. coast, confirmed N.Y.S.
      sceleratus L.
      flammula L.
      acris L.
      repens L.
Nymphaea alba L. In small inland lake. (L. Ordree)
Papaver rhoeas L.
      dubium L. sensu stricto, sparingly cornfields. Recorded in neighbouring Vice-counties, confirmed N.Y.S.
Fumaria bastardii Bor. Locally frequent on cultivated ground, det. R.D.M. & N.Y.S.
Nasturtium officinale R.Br.
Cardamine pratensis L.
Cochlearia officinalis L. forma, det.R.D.M. & N.Y.S.
      groenlandica L. sec Praeger? C. scotica Druce, det. R.D.M. Recorded Sherkin I. Praeger 1934. [*C. officinalis* subsp. *scotica*]
[Armoracia lapathifolia Gilib. [*A. rusticana*] close to ruined castle walls. May be a recent escape but probably of same age.] [author's brackets]
Sisymbrium officinale (L.) Scop.
Brassica campestris L.
      nigra (L.) Koch
Capsella bursa-pastoris (L) Medic.
Coronopus squamatus (Forsk) Aschers.
      didymus (L) Sm.
Cakile maritima Scop.
Raphanus maritimus Sm. One group of plants Tranaplous bay. Recorded for Sherkin Island J.J. Wolfe 1902.
Viola palustris L.
      arvensis agg. cultivated ground. Not previously recorded in this part of Ireland. Det.R.D.M.
      tricolor agg. Curtisii E.Forst var. On close turf & sand by the sea Tragowenmore bay. Det.R.D.M. N.Y.S.
      riviniana Rchb. Det. R.D.M. & N.Y.S.
Polygala serpyllifolia Hose. Det. R.D.M. & N.Y.S.
Saponaria officinalis L. One station on wall of cowshed.
Silene cucubulus Wibel.
      maritima (Hornem.) With.
Lychnis flos-cuculi L.
Agrostemma githago L. occasional, cornfields.
Cerastium vulgatum L.
      tetrandrum Curt. On rocky ledges by the sea Traguunslu [sic] Bay. Confirmed N.Y.S.
Stellaria media (L) Vill.
      graminea L.
      alsine Grimm.

Arenaria serpyllifolia L. confirmed N.Y.S.

    peploides. L.

Sagina maritima Sm. Rocky ledges very near sea Traguunslu [sic] By N.W. coast. Confirmed N.Y.S.

    procumbens L.

    nodosa (L) Fenzl. In short turf near the sea Trabawn Bay N.W. coast

Spergularia marginata (DC) Kittel.

    rupicola Lebel.

Montia fontana L. agg.

Elatine hexandra (Lapierre) DC. Small lake at extreme W. end of island.

Hypericum androsaemum L.

    quadrangulum L.

    pulchrum L.

    elodes L. In one small bog at W. end of island.

Althaea officinalis L. sparingly. Recorded Sherkin Island T. Allin 1883.

Lavatera arborea L.

Malva sylvestris L.

Radiola linoides Roth.

Linum catharticum L.

bienne Mill. One plant on sandy shore Tragowenmore.

Geranium molle L.

dissectum L.

robertianum L.

Erodium moschatum (L) Ait. One patch of plants close to farm buildings W. end of island. Recorded for
        Sherkin island T. Allin 1883. Det R.D.M. & N.Y.S.

Oxalis acetosella L.

[Acer pseudo-platanus L. planted for shelter.] [author's brackets]

Ulex europaeus L.

    gallii Planch.

Medicago lupulina L.

Trifolium pratense L.

    arvense L. On cliffs Abbey strand & S.E. coast. Recorded T. Allin 1883. R.A. Phillips 1900.

    repens L.

    campestre Schreb.

    dubium Sibth.

    filiforme L. [*T. micranthum*] Growing with T dubium in close turf near sea, one locality
        Traguunslu [sic] Bay N.W. coast. Recorded in adjacent vice-counties [Mid Cork and
        Kerry]. Confirmed N.Y.S.

Anthyllis vulneraria L.

    Var coccinea L. [Refers to the common red-flowered variant of this species in Co. Cork; var.
        coccinea L. is not recorded from Ireland] Apparently more frequent than type.

Lotus corniculatus L.

    uliginosus Schkuhr.

Ornithopus perpusillus L. A few plants on cliffs above Abbey strand. Not previously recorded in this
        part of the vice-county.

Vicia hirsuta (L) S.F. Gray.

    cracca L.

    sepium L.

    [sativa L. Obviously escaped from cultivation but well established along edges of fields and waste
        places. More frequent than V angustifolia. Confirmed N.Y.S.] [author's brackets]

Vicia angustifolia L. confirmed N.Y.S.

Lathyrus pratensis L.

Prunus spinosa L.
Filipendula ulmaria (L) Maxim.
Potentilla sterilis (L) Garke.
      erecta (L) Räusch.
      erecta x P. reptans [deleted by author] L. P. reptans was not recorded on the island but it was seen
            on the mainland.
      anserina L.
Comarum palustre L. [*Potentilla palustris*]
Alchemilla arvensis (L) Scop.
Umbilicus pendulinus DC. [*U. rupestris*] Frequent lane sides.
Sedum anglicum Huds.
Drosera rotundifolia L.
Hippuris vulgaris L. Lakelet by sea Trabawn Bay NW coast, one station.
Myriophyllum spicatum L. confirmed N.Y.S.
      alterniflorum confirmed N.Y.S.
Callitriche stagnalis Scop.
      intermedia Hoffm det R.D.M. & N.Y.S.
Peplis portula L. [*Lythrum portula*]
Lythrum salicaria L.
Epilobium parviflorum Schreb. confirmed G.M.A.
      obscurum Schreb. confirmed G.M.A.
      palustre L.
[Fuchsia riccartonii hort. [*F. magellanica*] Well established along some stone walls.] [author's brackets]
Hydrocotyle vulgaris L.
Eryngium maritimum L.
Conium maculatum L.
Smyrnium olusatrum L. Near ruined Abbey.
Apium nodiflorum (L) Lag
      inundatum (L) Rchb.f.
Petroselinum crispum (Mill) Nym. On ruined castle and Abbey walls. Det. R.D.M. & N.Y.S.
Anthriscus sylvestris (L) Hoffm.)
Crithmum maritimum L. occasional
Oenanthe lachenelii C.C. Gmel. rare Kinish harbour
      crocata L.
Heracleum sphondylium L.
Daucus carota L.
Torilis anthriscus (L) C.C. Gmel. [*T. japonica*]
Hedera helix L.
Sambucus nigra L.
Lonicera periclymenum L.
Rubia peregrina L. one plant, lane side near Abbey strand.
Galium verum L.
      saxatile L.
      palustre L.
      aparine L.
Sherardia arvensis L.
Valeriana dentata L. Poll. confirmed N.Y.S.
Succisa pratensis Moench.
Knautia arvensis (L) Coult.
Eupatorium cannabinum L. two stations near Abbey strand.

Solidago virgaurea L.

Bellis perennis L.

Aster tripolium L.

Gnaphalium uliginosum L.

Pulicaria dysenterica (L) Bernh.

Achillea millefolium L.

Anthemis nobilis L. abundant [*Chamaemelum nobile*]

Chrysanthemum leucanthum L. [*Leucanthemum vulgare*]

Matricaria maritima L.

      matricarioides (Less) Porter. [*M. discoidea*] frequent along lanes & waste ground.

Artemisia absinthium L. recorded Sherkin Island R.A. Phillips.

      vulgaris L.

Tussilago farfara L.

Senecio vulgaris L.

      sylvaticus L. det. R.D.M. & N.Y.S.

      jacobea L.

Arctium vulgare (Hill) A.H. Evans

Carduus pycnocephalus L. [probably in error for *P. tenuiflorus*]

Circium [sic] vulgare (Savi) Ten.

      palustre (L) Scop.

      arvense (L) Scop.

Centaurea nigra L.

Lapsana communis L.

Crepis capillaris (L) Wallr.

Hieracium pilosella L. agg. [*Pilosella officinarum*]

Hypochoeris radicata L.

Leontodon leysseri (Wallr) Beck. [*L.taraxacoides*]

      autumnalis L.

Taraxacum officinale Weber.

Sonchus oleraceus L.

      asper (L) Hill.

      arvensis L.

Jasione montana L.

Calluna vulgaris (L) Hull

Erica tetralix L.

      cinerea L.

Limonium humile Mill. confirmed N.Y.S.

Armeria maritima Willd.

Primula vulgaris Huds.

Anagallis arvensis L.

      tenella (L) Murr.

Centunculus minimus L. [*Anagallis minima*]

Samolus valerandi L.

Fraxinus excelsior L.

Cicendia filiformis (L) Delarb. locally abundant in damp and boggy ground. This species is at its northern limit. It occurs only in Cork and Kerry.

Centaurium pulchellum (Sw) E.H.L. Krause ?untypical form det. R.D.M. & N.Y.S. Turf Trabawn Bay [Polunin (1950) did not include this record, suggesting a change of opinion]

Menyanthes trifoliata L.

Symphytum officinale L.

Myosotis caespitosa K.F. Schultz.

secunda A. Murr.

arvensis (L) Hill.

Calystegia sepium (L) R.Br.

Convolvulus arvensis L.

Lycium chinense Mill.

Verbascum thapsus L.

Linaria elatine (L) Mill. [*Kickxia elatine*] frequent on cultivated ground.

Scrophularia aquatica L.

Digitalis purpurea L.

Veronica persica Poir. confirmed N.Y.S.

arvensis L.

chamaedrys L.

scutellata L.

beccabunga L.

Euphrasia officinalis L. agg. locally abundant.

Odontites rubra Gilib. [*O. verna*]

Parentucellia viscosa (L) Caruel. frequent in marshy ground near sea particularly SW end of island.

Pedicularis sylvatica L.

Rhinanthus minor l. agg.

*Utricularia neglecta Lehm. abundant in one small lake near the sea, Trabawn Bay NW coast. Recorded in adjacent vice-counties. Det. R.D.M. & N.Y.S.

Pinguicula lusitanica L.

Verbena officinalis L.

Mentha longifolia (L) Huds. one station Tranaplous bay.

aquatica L.

pulegium L.

Lycopus europaeus L.

Thymus serpyllum L. agg. [*T. praecox*]

Glecoma [sic] hederacea L.

Scutellaria minor Huds.

Prunella vulgaris L.

Stachys palustris L.

sylvatica L.

arvensis (L) L.

Galeopsis tetrahit L. [sensu lato]

Lamium hybridum Vill.

Teucrium scorodonia L.

Plantago coronopus L.

maritima L.

lanceolata L.

major L.

Littorella uniflora (L) Aschers. lakelet W end of island.

Chenopodium album L. det R.D.M. & N.Y.S.

Beta maritima L.

Atriplex patula L. det. R.D.M. & N.Y.S.

hastata L. [*A. prostrata* DC.]

babingtonii [*A. glabriuscula*]

* laciniata L. bay with pebbles Kinish harbour; one station only. Previously recorded on the East coast of Ireland only. Det. R.D.M. & N.Y.S.

Salicornia europaea L.

Suaeda maritima (L) Dum.

Salsola kali L.

Polygonum convolvulus L. [*Fallopia convolvulus*]

    aviculare L. agg.

    raii Bab. [*P. oxyspermum* subsp. *raii*]

    hydropiper l. [*Persicaria hydropiper*]

    persicaria [*Persicaria maculosa*]

    amphibium L. [*Persicaria amphibia*]

Rumex conglomeratus Murr.

    obtusifolius L.

    crispus L.

    acetosa L.

    acetosella L.

Euphorbia helioscopia L.

    hyberna L. frequent lane-sides.

    peplus L.

Humulus lupulus L. cliffs close to ruined abbey.

Urtica dioica L.

    urens L.

Parietaria diffusa Mert & Koch. [*P. judaica*]

Salix repens L. agg.

Spiranthes spiralis (L) Chevall. frequent on close turf near sea. Previously recorded from Sherkin island
        T. Allin 1883.

Iris pseudacorus L.

Scilla non-scripta (L) Hoffmgg. & Link. [Hyacinthoides non-scriptus]

Narthecium ossifragum (L) Huds.

Juncus bufonius L.

    gerardii Lois.

    effusus L.

    conglomeratus L. rare only two plants found

    maritimus Lam.

    bulbosus L.

    articulatus L.

    acutiflorus LHoffm.

Luzula multiflora (Retz) Lej. var congesta (Thuill) Koch. Det R.D.M. & N.Y.S.

Typha latifolia L.

Sparganium erectum [deleted by author] L. not confirmed

    simplex [deleted by author] Huds. neglectum [*S. erectum* subsp. *neglectum*]

Lemna minor L.

Baldellia ranunculoides (L) Parl.

Triglochin palustris L.

    maritima L.

Potamogeton crispus L.

    pectinatus L. confirmed N.Y. S.

Ruppia maritima L. lakelet W. end of island, one station.

Eleocharis palustris (L) Roem & Schult.

    multicaulis (Sm) Sm.

Scirpus fluitans L.

    cernuus Vahl. Tragunnslu [sic] Bay

    setaceus L.

    lacustris l. [*S. lacustris* subsp. *lacustris*]

tabernaemontani C.C.Gmel. [*S. lacustris* subsp. *tabernaemontani*]

maritimus L.

Eriophorum angustifolium Honck.

Schoenus nigricans L. one station, bog W. end of island.

Carex pulicaris L.

arenaria L. confirmed E.N.

paniculata L.

vulpina L. [*C. otrubae*]

leporina L.

nigra (L) Richard

panicea L confirmed E.N.

distans L. confirmed E.N.

extensa Good.

tumidocarpa Anderss. determined E.N.

* pseudocyparus L. two stations lakelets SW end of island. L. Ordree & Trabawn Bay. Not before recorded in the extreme South West of Ireland. Confirmed E.N.

Anthoxanthum odoratum L.

Alopecurus geniculatus L.

Agrostis stolonifera L. var stolonifera (L) Koch det. C.E.H.

Agrostis tenuis Sibth. det C.E.H. [*A. capillaris*]

Ammophila arenaria (L) Link.

Aira caryophyllea L.

Holcus lanatus L.

Arrhenatherum elatius (L) J & C Presl.

Sieglingia decumbens (L) Bernh.

Phragmites communis Trin.

Cynosurus cristatus L.

Molinia caerulea (L) Moench

Catabrosa aquatica (L) Beauv. var. littoralis Parnell. one station on sandy shore, Trabawn Bay NW coast. Det. C.E.H.

Dactylis glomerata L.

Poa annua L.

trivialis L.

Glyceria fluitans (L) R. Br.

Desmazeria marina (L) Druce frequent on ruined buildings. Det. C.E.H.

Vulpia myuros (L) Gmel

bromoides (L) F.S. Gray

Festuca ovina L. determined C.E.H.

Bromus ramosus Huds.

hordeaceus L.

mollis L.

Brachypodium sylvaticum (Huds) Beauv.

Lolium perenne L.

* [multiflorum Lam. frequent in long grass surrounding fields. Det. C.E. H.] [author's brackets]

temulentum

Agropyron repens (L) Beauv.

junceum (L) Beauv.

Osmunda regalis L.

Pteridium aquilinum (L) Kuhn.

Blechnum spicant (L) Roth

Asplenium adiantum-nigrum L.

marinum L.
     trichomanes L.
Phyllitis scolopendrium (L) Newm.
Dryopteris felix-mas L. agg.
     dilatata (Hoffm) A. Gray
Polypodium vulgare L.
Equisetum arvense L.
     fluviatile L.

The following plants have been recorded from Sherkin Island but were not seen by me August 1947.
Fumaria muralis L. R.A. Phillips fide A. Bennett 1896
Erodium maritimum (L) Ait. R.A. Phillips?
Eryngium campestre L. Field on Sherkin Island J.J. Wolfe & R.A. Phillips?
Torilis nodosa (L) Gaertn T. Allin 1883
Lamium amplexicaule L. T. Allin 1883. I saw this plant on Hare Island in 1947
Rumex pulcher L. R.A. Phillips 1896-1902
Carex muricata ? T. Allin 1883.
* = new vice-county [West Cork] record.

APPENDIX 2. Unpublished agricultural notes by Oleg Polunin

Agricultural notes

Fields are dug over every 10-12 yrs depending on number of fields on farm. Uusally the oldest are dug & rotation is as follows:

potatoes - corn - ley with 2-3 years of hay cutting - semipermanent ley 7 yrs

Ulex [Gorse] is cut as fodder for Horses. There used to be Sheep over Slievemore but now not an economic proposition.

O'Driscolls' rotation [probably M.F. O'Driscoll]

1 yr   Potatoes 5 furrows left & two taken out on each side & sods placed green to green

Potatoes planted on raised ridges (5 furrows) broad & earth from second digging from (2).

When potatoes are sprouting above ground [, a] further spit placed on raised ridge.

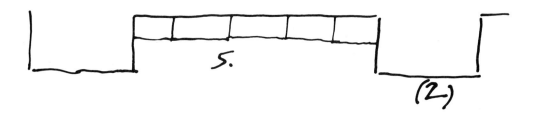

2nd year   Wheat sown in the spring. Broadcast sown on the ploughed alternate furrow. Then harrowed with blackthorn [towing a thorn bush behind horses or later a tractor was a traditional method of harrowing in Ireland and Britain] & flattened out. When corn about 6" high [,] seed of grass (Rye grass & Italian Rye grass) scattered among the growing corn and then reharrowed with blackthorn. Thus the corn is seeded & no further cultivation is necessary after cutting corn.

3rd year   Hay - after 2 cuttings re spring & re autumn

4 yr   Hay cutting

5 yr   Grazing

6 year   Grazing

Manuring. Cow byre lined with 'silver' [strand] sand as bedding in summer, mixed with straw in winter. This is thrown on to the ley before ploughing. A layer of seaweed laid over the potatoes (after) planting.

Marginal pastures not normally cultivated & passes over into heathland.

Note Oats sometimes take place of Wheat. Also Swedes [and] Turnips planted in same stage as potatoes.

INDEX OF LATIN NAMES

(Numbers indicate those assigned in the Systematic List, except those with p., which indicate page numbers)

INNÉACS DE NA hAINMNEACHA GAEILGE

INDEX OF ENGLISH NAMES